525

D1492477

THE TEACH YOURSELF BOOKS
EDITED BY LEONARD CUTTS

ECONOMIC GEOGRAPHY

in the
GEOGRAPHY
Section

Prepared under the special
direction and scientific
Editorship of

PROFESSOR FRANK DEBENHAM
Cambridge University

TEACH YOURSELF GEOGRAPHY

Uniform with this book
and completing the series in five volumes

THE USE OF GEOGRAPHY
(Key Volume)
by F. Debenham

PHYSICAL GEOGRAPHY
by R. F. Peel

BIOGEOGRAPHY
by M. S. Anderson

HISTORICAL GEOGRAPHY
by J. B. Mitchell

ECONOMIC GEOGRAPHY

By
W. S. THATCHER, M.A.

THE ENGLISH UNIVERSITIES PRESS LIMITED
ST. PAUL'S HOUSE, WARWICK SQUARE
LONDON

First Printed 1949

*Made and Printed in Great Britain for The English Universities Press,
Ltd., London, by C. Tinling & Co., Ltd., Liverpool, London and Prescot.*

A GENERAL INTRODUCTION TO THE SERIES

IN planning a series of volumes to be called *Teach Yourself Geography*, it was necessary for me, as Editor, to choose between alternatives, and I want you to understand why I made the decision I did and what we have set out to do.

It would have been possible to adopt the delightful, and very successful, method used by the English Universities Press historians, who present each volume in their series as the story of a period based upon the life of a great man. Our geography series might well have had the pattern of a Place and its People for each book until the world was covered. The result would have been a new series of Regional Geographies which, though useful, would have been mainly descriptive in character and not fundamental to the subject. They would have been a loose pile of stones rather than a masonry structure keyed together to make a building.

Now, geography was described by one of its greatest recent exponents as not so much a subject as a point of view. With that in mind, I decided it was better to take the other alternative : to lead readers to the top of the mountain whence they could get that view, rather than just give them a series of peeps at individual parts of the landscape.

In my key volume, I set out to provide the incentive for that climb, outlining the route and giving a general idea of the prospect at the summit. The title of the book is *The Use of Geography*, and if interest, contentment and an increased power of judgment are sufficient rewards, then geography is useful indeed. You will find I have dealt mainly with the structure of the subject and its aim, with hints as to the ways and means of achieving some part of it : an understanding of Place in all its bearings. My chief object was to show that geography is for everyone, and that it is full of interest at every stage, and that it is a practical subject.

The four companion volumes concern themselves more closely with technique—if such a formidable word can be used to describe the approach to each of the divisions into which geography can be conveniently separated for the purpose of study.

Thus Mr. Peel's book deals with the physical background ; those aspects of air, land and water which, quite independently of man, affect the environment in which we live, and which are almost, but not quite, beyond our control. He points the way towards learning about the inanimate world around us, and his treatment of this branch of the subject is as thorough as the length of the book will permit.

Mrs. Anderson in her *Biogeography* deals with the animate side of environment, culminating in the highest of the animals, Man himself. In some ways she is opening up a new development of Geography, or at least a new focussing point, for you will find that she emphasises the biological influences which constantly affect man for good or ill and which have in large measure determined where and how he lives ; why he varies so much in appearance, and even in character. Her vivid style is well suited to such a fresh viewpoint. If this book is a study of man as an animal living under essentially the same biological controls as other animals, then Mr. Thatcher leads us to consider man as a highly organised social being with trade between places and peoples as a dominating control.

He calls his book *Economic Geography*, an experiment. Each of these volumes is an experiment—and certainly if it is an experiment to take an apparently intricate subject like this and reduce it to a lively simplicity by talking to his reader as he might at his own fireside, then we could do with many more such experiments. Even such a forbidding subject as the Mechanism of Exchange can become absorbing when chatted about by a kindly tutor possessed of a cheerful pessimism and an infinite understanding. The case for Economic Geography rests very safely in his hands.

Finally, the geographer must look back as well as forward if he is to study fully the interaction between Place and Man. The geographies of the past are in some respects the most powerful influences which mould the geography of the present. Miss Mitchell deals in a scholarly way with these in her *Historical Geography*. Because it is a new line of approach she has to spend some time in explaining what it is and is not. The rewards are great, for when rightly understood there is something peculiarly fascinating in tracing the Past in the Present, in viewing Place, whether on parish- or country-scale, as determined very largely by what has happened before. This volume should put Historical Geography very firmly on its feet as an integral part of the subject as a whole and one which any reader can share in and profit by.

Lastly, I should like to explain that this series is a combined effort. One of the reasons for selecting the authors from my own staff was so that we could work together as a team. Yet even frequent consultation is not in itself sufficient to achieve agreement and a common point of view, and it is as much the personality of my authors as their knowledge that is responsible for the unity we hope will appear in the separate volumes of this series. I am, in fact, proud to introduce to the general reader these members of a staff who have made my duty easy not only as Editor, but in the more arduous capacity of running the large department of which they form a part.

FRANK DEBENHAM

The Department of Geography,
   The University,
     Cambridge.

CONTENTS

PREFACE

THIS book is an experiment. When asked to write it I greatly hesitated and not the least of my several reasons for so doing was that I am afraid of small books. To compress so large a subject within so small a space must mean either an over-simplification or grave distortion and as has been remarked elsewhere little books are useful only when one has read the large ones. Many people have not the time for the larger books but still wish to know something about economic geography while beginners can get lost if given the advanced books. For this reason I consented to try my hand here though I warned those who are responsible for publication that they ran a risk.

Having decided to write I found I had the option of making as neat a précis as I could of what is called Economic Geography so that the reader could read straight on if he were not too bored or I could try to really teach. It is, however, one thing to teach personally and another to do so through the written word, yet I am daring to adopt the same method which I follow when teaching a class of students. When so doing I have always presumed they could read for themselves and so suggest books and reading. There are plenty of books with which to start, the titles of some will be found in my introductory chapter. These books are of sufficient size to give the necessary outline but even they cannot have everything within their covers. One book is good for certain subjects, another for others and the earnest student must be aware of this. Then when they have read, students must write and it is in the correcting of essays that most of my teaching is done. The essays are read aloud so that the other students can listen and be ready to criticise or ask

questions. While the essay is being read I criticise. A statement is made and I demand where it came from: who was the
authority and had he the right to pose as such. It is necessary
to teach the student to be alert. Most students still come with
the misconception that education is the acquisition of facts and
will silently beseech one to give them notes. That method is
no use, as education has to do with thinking though naturally
facts must be used. That is why the reader will look in vain for
a systematic presentation of facts in this book. That is not its
purpose though I shall indicate where they may be found. So
my supervision can be an agitated affair. It is astonishing how
uncritical even good students can be though after all it is perfectly
natural. One is oneself for most things. Criticism is not
merely a negative thing it must be positive. If a piece of work
is good then it must be acknowledged good. As the essay
reading proceeds I fire questions at the reader and make him
defend himself. It is easy to practice scientific detachment
when studying botany or entomology as one's data is purely
objective. A French marigold does not arouse any patriotic
antagonism and one can even contemplate the shamrock as such
with a dispassionate eye, but to be scientific about human beings
and their doings is another matter. Can an economist be
neutral? If not he must at least be trained to be honest. It
does not necessarily follow that all who cannot agree with the
Labour Party are vermin nor does it follow that all who are not
right-wing Conservatives are necessarily what you will. One
of the best compliments ever paid to me consisted in a joint
accusation by two students, one of whom was a Conservative
and the other a Socialist. They both accused me of trying to
pervert their political faith. I felt that I must be holding the
scales fairly honestly but one would be dishonest to pretend
that one had no bias. No doubt the reader will glimpse it as
he goes on. But one must insist when teaching one's students
that examination of all data must be dispassionate and honest.
There is no room for politics in scholarship.

Not only do I ask questions but I offer suggestions. From
time to time it is necessary to give a more or less lengthy explanation and all the time I am trying to make the student look round

the question. Indeed that is not putting it well. Most economic problems are not round but present a great number of facets. What makes the 'practical' man so dangerous is that he may see one facet or even two very clearly and correctly. This leads him to believe he has seen the whole problem whereas he has seen probably very little. If for instance one is studying British farming it is necessary to look elsewhere for parallels and contrasts. Generally the parallels are not really so and one must be aware of it. No son is exactly the double of his father though he may be very like him. His mother had something to do with his make-up, not to mention his long line of ancestors, but he may be like enough to draw certain conclusions. So apparently I jump from one place to another and the reader may wonder what I am doing. In a class if I fail to make myself clear the pupil can immediately ask what I do mean. The reader has not this privilege. One of my colleagues has said she often cannot follow the line of my argument in some of the chapters she has very kindly read. The answer is that in many places there is no argument but only a series of *obiter dicta*, hints thrown out to the pupil. The reader must be patient and be prepared to play my game and I am demanding a lot from him, but I am paying him a preliminary compliment of supposing that he is intelligent and prepared to put some work and thought into his reading. I don't think I am interested in the person who wants me to do all the work. After all one can only teach: the pupil must learn.

There is no doubt that even the highly intelligent person needs a teacher when he is beginning a subject and it is no disparagement to say so. I have taught a good few people between the two wars and since, many of whom have and had far better heads than I and who are now quite eminent people in their own line. You soon know if a pupil has a better brain than yourself and he too soon knows it. I tell such should they be impatient that I am useful as someone with whom they can spar while learning to box. You can't bluff university students, nor boys for that matter, and they are critical. If you don't know a thing they are aware of it very soon. One doesn't really know very much and the best way to teach is to act as a guide, a first among equals. So with my readers I am asking that they will take a hint, pick up a suggestion and then follow it up by reading in some of the suggested books.

There is not a chapter which could not be expanded into a large book or indeed into a shelf full of books so I am bound to compress, and anyhow I don't know enough to write an authoritative work on railways, shipping, currency and the hundred and one other matters included under the title of economic geography, nor is it my business to do so both because these books already exist and because the function of the geographer is a different one, that of showing the inter-relationship of all these against the regional background. Not that he always succeeds. I think that too often we attempt too much, for who can know about the whole world?

I have also been accused of being too staccato in my writing: the sentences are too short and on occasion there is no verb. The latter omission I have tried to rectify and I hope there are not too many missing verbs but the former alleged fault I must defend on two grounds. This is not an academic thesis partly, I suspect, because I am not very academic myself but chiefly because it is an experiment. I am trying to talk to my reader as I talk to my pupils. I break in on what he is saying by adding a comment, by querying a statement. All the time I am challenging him to think and in so doing I do not always 'keep to the subject'. There is a vast difference between coaching and supervision. In the former one is paid to hand over the 'stuff' for examination purposes: one is a crammer and I have no use for crammers. The supervisor is there to direct and guide. To do his work properly he must know his pupil and how his pupil's mind works. You cannot teach well if you do not know your pupils. That is why big classes are an evil. To know your pupil you must talk to him and what is at least as important let him talk to you. You must find out what he knows and doesn't know, which means you will have to talk about everything under the sun. So I have talked and some of the things I have said may not appear to be economic geography, but then I have covered myself by saying there is no such subject.

All these separate chapters will at first seem to have little reference to each other and will appear very disjointed but I have a definite idea what I want to do. Whether I shall succeed I do not know but I ask the reader to be patient. One's pupils always complain that the various subjects and lectures given at the School of Geography in their first term bewilder them and they can't see how it all fits together. All one can reply is that if they will go on steadily the tag-ends will gradually come together in an organised body of knowledge. May I say the same to my reader. Take as an example of what I mean, the aero engine. During the war one of the many things would-be pilots had to learn about was the engine upon which their lives would depend. They had in the instruction centres 'exploded' engines, i.e. engines with parts cut away or dissembled so that the pupil could learn first what each part was like and then how it fitted in with the rest to make the whole engine. But that was not all, one really understands an engine if one can visualise it in motion and see in one's mind's eye the position of each part of the mechanism in relation to each other part at any given moment. It takes time to learn all that. So with geography: we pull the engine to pieces and cut away the cylinder walls, taking each part one by one. Then it must be assembled and started up. Only the economic machine is much more delicate and intricate than any mechanism made of steel.

May I therefore warn my reader how much I rely upon him to take a hint and to be ready for the numerous interpolated remarks. These are no more than a tutor's talks: they are not a closely argued theme nor are they intended to do more than teach one how to go about the job of learning. It would have been as well if this book had been entitled 'Some introductory hints on economic geography' for it is no more than that. The beginner need not bother about the larger works though even he should know from where the statements come. The acquisition of knowledge requires effort: it can not be made easy beyond a limited point, but then no good thing is ever given away nor should be. I can only hope that I may succeed in this experiment.

I have to acknowledge the kind permission to use certain tables taken from the *Board of Trade Journal* and certain U.N.O.

publications.   Also a table taken from Professor J. H. Richardson's book *British Economic Policy,* and from Mr. A. R. Prest's recent book.   I am grateful to all for their permission.

Fitzwilliam House   W. S. THATCHER.
        Cambridge.

CHAPTER I

INTRODUCTION

Actually there is no such subject as Economic Geography any more than there is Historical or Political. There is only Geography, but this is too much for us to comprehend so we break it up into sections for our convenience. One can go even further and declare that there is no such thing as Geography or History or what you will: there is knowledge. That, however, does not help us much so we must make the best of our human limitations which means that we must specialise. What we must do is to be aware of the liberties we are taking and then we shall be on our guard against the sin of pride. There might be a case for the Physical and even Regional geographers who could put up a defence for their specialised subjects, at least the Physical geographer could though I don't think he could defend himself for long. The Regional geographer would have a bad time from the start and one must not say much about him here as one of my colleagues in a companion volume proposes to give him that bad time. But specialisation in the human side is a desperately dangerous thing as human life and its manifestations are so complex and so delicately and subtly interwoven. Here one must constantly stop one's specialised study to look at the whole. One must not only study economic geography or even geography, one must read history, philosophy though much of it is verbiage, religion though much may be false and anything which gives one insight into human motives. Not least one should read novels.

For present purposes we may briefly divide Geography into (1) Physiography which will include Climatology and Oceanography, (2) Plant Geography. These are supposed to lead up to (3) Regional Geography about which I must make a few qualifying remarks. These three studies deal with the non-human side of our subject. They could be studied by a visitor from Mars even though the human race did not exist just as we try to study the moon or Mars itself.   On the human side we have (4) Anthropogeography an unpleasant term and open to discussion, (5) Historical Geography in which is included the history of geographical study.   These combined with regional geography lead up to the final study, (6) Economic Geography.

Classification is always a difficult and arbitrary thing.   We are compelled to classify in order to get on with our study but should be aware of the danger.   Marshall in his *Principles of Economics* gives his readers warning of this in the little Latin quotation in the title page of his book 'Natura non facit saltum' which might be rendered 'There are no breaks in Nature'.   A warning which is more necessary today than ever before when planners and their kind think they are being scientific when they classify.   In real life things blur into each other though it is vastly important to distinguish between a blur and a smudge. As a test take the following terms: a baby, a child, a young man, a middle aged man, an elderly man, and an old man.   Where does each phase begin and end? So to return, our classification is made merely for our convenience and nothing more.   It is as well, however, that we should use phrases which everyone understands and I must look for a moment at the term Regional. Originally the term applied to 'a part of the world's surface which had obvious unity but which was not a political unit and had no place name'.   The Mediterranean lands are a typical example but this concept soon became very blurred or rather smudged when people began to say what they thought the words meant.   Miss Mitchell sums the discussion up as follows: 'The natural region should mean the region as it is as the result of the interaction of all those elements of place that are not man made however much altered by him.   In contrast to this there is the "geographical" region: it again means what it says, the region as it is as a result of the interaction of all the elements of place including those that are man made'.   I shall use the term in the first sense though I warn my reader that the distinction between the natural and the geographical is man made or in this case woman made and so is not like the laws of the Medes and Persians.

The economic geographer has before him a formidable task

for he must be both an economist and a geographer. He ought to know something of the principles of economics, of the structure of industry, of the organisation of commerce and trade. He should know his regional geography in both the senses in which the word is used. Well might the reader hesitate at so formidable a prospect, but he can take comfort in that nobody knows very much not even those who devote most of their time to study. Nor is this ignorance confined to those who study and teach geography. None of us knows much, a thing to remember as it will help to keep us modest. Modesty is a flower which all scientists should cultivate with care lest we fall into the very errors we condemn. But there is a further reason for attempting our study. Today we are all in a responsible position as people with votes which must be cast this way or that. The issues are vital and urgent and will not admit of delay. The Gallup poll always has a third group, the 'Don't know's'. These people are merely leaving the decision to someone else. In the brave new world which is to be created the geographer and the economic geographer ought to have much to say.

What then does our subject include and where does it start? It starts where regional and anthropological geography leave off. Regional geography tells us Nature's layout: the nature of the terrain with its mineral endowment, the vegetation and the animal life which it sustains and which are so closely conditioned by the climatic factors. It is quite impossible to begin our study without a good regional background. Without it one is reduced to an endless collection of uninteresting facts, that penguins come from the Antarctic, polar bears from the Arctic, coals from Newcastle and ships from the Clyde. Economic geography is much more than a quartermaster's list of goods, useful as such lists can be. So we must know our regions well, bearing in mind that they are only clearly defined in geography books never in nature. Given this knowledge we shall not only know certain facts, and facts are useful, but we shall be able to feel the accuracy of certain kinds of statement though not every kind. For instance we would not expect to find grapes growing in the open in Iceland nor expect maize to be a success in Scotland. I can see no reason why we should not make a guess that penguins are found in the Arctic and polar-bears in the Antarctic though no doubt zoologists might smile wisely. Hence the necessity of checking our deductions by observation. Not that everyone can visit both the ice-caps though some reliable people can do so and tell us what they have seen. One might visit Newcastle and its neighbourhood or even the Clyde. All the time one must be observing. Economic geography is no bookish or theoretical study.

It is fairly straightforward studying the major regions, the difficulty begins in the transitional zones. The Mediterranean region is one of the stock examples. Let us consider it for a moment, as economic geographers not as regional geographers, for our job is to take their data and then start on our particular study. The characteristics of the Mediterranean region are its hot, dry summers and cool, moist winters, the marked and rapid contrasts in relief, mountains and hills and valleys. There are no great plains lending themselves to easy and mechanical cultivation but only small patches here and there. There are practically no minerals at least in quantities. The vegetation is characteristic: it is drought resisting using all the tricks and devices which nature employs and most of the vegetation is not of much use to man, but that is not unusual anywhere as any unhappy gardener knows. That is not all. It is a region of vivid sunshine, of clear cut demarcation between light and shade, of sparkling clearness. Many of my readers will have seen it. A delectable region. Would that one could return to it. But what has beauty and sunshine to do with economics? We need to be practical. It has a great deal to do with it as living is more than making a living and a world without beauty is no world. Let us return to what we were considering. This region lacks water just when is is required, but given water can grow a great variety of things. Here we find the vine, the olive, the mulberry, citrus fruits. Notice that these are all tree crops which can put their roots down deep in search of moisture. Wheat and barley grow well but they must have water so man has practiced both irrigation and dry farming. It is a region unfavourable to pastoral farming as we understand it as the summer drought is fatal to grass. Some cattle are kept in a few favoured spots and transhumance is practised. All that and more we must know. Then knowing it we shall be able to identify other similar regions as in California, the Peninsula in South Africa, Western Australia. The geographer will tell you why they are where they are and why they have the characteristics they have. We shall expect to find a similar vegetation in all these regions and will, though we shall not find identical plants and animals. Nature is prolific and likes finding diverse solutions to the same problem and in this she differs from the race of planners who hate anything being different. These recently discovered Mediterranean regions did not have olives and vines and fig trees though they can be and have been introduced. You see our geography enables us to make scientific guesses and gives us a reasonable and ordered world instead of the quartermaster's list.

Let us return to our Mediterranean world. It is by no means homogeneous. There are strong resemblances but nevertheless the African coast is more arid and harsher than the European side. It is beginning to merge into the semi-arid regions and already the hot breath of the desert can be felt. The Western half differs from the Eastern half so that altogether we have a considerable variety within the greater unity. Here then is or was a natural region into which man intruded at a very early age and in which he developed those great and magnificent civilisations from which we in North Western Europe are spiritually descended. For we moderns are the descendants of Greece, of Rome and of Palestine. From these we obtained our religion, our art and science and our law and administrative order. It is a region which has been modified by man's constant toil and effort so that it is no longer natural in the original sense. Yet man has modified it but little though if the reader is a purist we can call it a geographical region.

If we economic geographers are to study such a region we are still only partly equipped when we have studied the regional background. Something at least we must know of its peoples and their long history but more of their history than their physical characteristics. Here are peoples with a past which still lives so vividly that to neglect it is foolishness. We must turn to both the historian and the historical geographer for enlightenment, only then shall we be ready for our task as economic geographers.   Then we can measure the importance of the Suez Canal, the lack of the basic metals and the attitudes of the peoples themselves to modern industry with its dull regimentation in contrast to their own vivid living.   Two books may be read as an introduction, *The Mediterranean* by André Siegfried.   This is a most pleasant introduction to a pleasant study.   There is nothing profound in it and one need not accept all the author's statements or findings.   He too has been dazzled by its beauty.   The second is *The Mediterranean Lands* by Marion I. Newbigin, which is an introduction to the human and historical geography.   It is a more serious piece of work than Siegfried's but is none the less pleasant as well as instructive reading.

So one turns from 'the' Mediterranean lands to the Mediterranean regions already mentioned which have been peopled only recently, at least by the white peoples.   The physical backgrounds are similar, the human completely different.   The historical background of these new Mediterraneans is to be found chiefly in the countries from which their recently settled peoples have migrated.   They are mainly Anglo-Saxon or American except in Chili, and they have brought their own values and thoughts.   The economic geographer will have a lot of questions to ask about the Mediterranean countries after he has listed their productions and trade.   He will be asking how much change is possible, an impossible question, but one must constantly ask questions which cannot be answered.   One should note that all the great questions in life have no answer, yet it is more important to ask them than to ask the little questions which can be answered and which are so dull.   He will be watching what changes have taken place, noticing the rate of change and its limitations.   A very little economic geography on Mussolini's part might have saved the Italians much suffering.

Now let us pass by contrast to the tropical forest region of Africa which stretches along the west coast from Sierra Leone to the mouth of the Congo, and which occupies much of the Congo Basin.   The rainfall averages over 60 inches a year which falls throughout the year while the temperature is uniformly high never falling below 75° F. This hot steaming atmosphere results in a most luxuriant plant growth. At one time this region was supposed to cover a much larger area than it is now known to do, nevertheless the estimated area is 875,000 square miles, about 7·9 of the continent. It is very well described in M.I. Newbigin's *Plant and Animal Geography*, chapter VII. A similar but larger region is that in the Amazon Basin. Here the rainfall is much heavier and the flooding on a far more extensive scale. When comparing these two regions we find that they are similar in their response to nature. Both have the same major characteristics, viz. (1) the multiciplicity of tree species in contrast to the temperate forests where one finds large stands of the same tree, (2) the marked stratification of tree growth, there being several tiers of trees in addition to a ground growth, (3) the number and variety of climbers. The total result is an impenetrable growth which combined with the heavy flooding and disease have made these areas practically impossible to man. Where man has crept in he has done so entirely on Nature's terms and these have been more than harsh. For a description of the Amazon forest Duguid's *Green Hell* is a vivid account, but no description however good will give one any real idea of what such places are like. You must go and see.

Here then is a totally different kind of region to the one we have just considered. Here is Nature in one of her prolific moods, creating and killing, recklessly, prodigiously and at a tempo with which man has been unable to cope until very recently, and even yet he only works on the fringe. Read *The Village in the Jungle* by Leonard Woolf, the story of which is laid in Ceylon. Also *Tales from the Outposts—Jungle Tales* edited by Blackwoods. Both are vivid and excellent.

The economic geographer notes that here few civilisations have arisen and these great areas, in the main, have been and still are useless. Once a little rubber was collected at vast human expense, but it could never have been enough while the difficulties were so great that man turned to Malaya and other more manageable places. Now that tropical medicine has made such vast strides and the new mechanisms make it possible to handle development works as never before, it may be that they will be brought into use. All they await is a great demand and this might come should the teeming millions of Asia find the wherewithal to buy.

One has taken two strong examples and treated them very roughly and superficially. That is all one can do here in so small a book. Each great region demands attention in a similar way but there is much more to be done. Regions are vague things and men don't live and work in regions just like that but in political communities in which they fence themselves off from their fellows, keeping to themselves those bounties which Nature has provided or making do if she has been niggardly. There are two possible ways out of this maldistribution of Nature's gifts, or maybe three. They are migration, trade and population limitation, about which something will be said in later chapters, but we must note that in general the human race is not given to hearty co-operation, rather, its major efforts seem to be directed in the opposite direction. The frustrations all go to prove that man is not primarily an economic nor a greatly thinking animal, but rather a creature of emotion subject to passions and conditioned reflexes. These non-economic factors will also be glanced at in due course.

So far we have spoken of man as if there were no such things as races, of groupings of peoples, of differences in cultures and in technical abilities. In reality we find the human race divided and split up in a multitude of ways, some are highly civilised, though in diverse ways, some are primitive peoples equally diverse. At one time it was firmly held that certain races were superior and others inferior, the white peoples for instance were pre-eminently mechanically minded and inventive: the black peoples were definitely inferior, while the yellow and brown peoples came in between. That belief has been greatly modified during this century by the achievements of the Japanese and by a fuller understanding of the various Oriental civilisations. Even towards the African, attitudes are changing though slowly. Here we come into the domain of the anthropologist and we need his assistance. At the moment there are many questions to which we do not know the answer, but even if with Rousseau we premise that all men are born equal, it does not alter the fact that education or lack of education, using the term in the broadest and deepest sense, causes vast differences in abilities and tastes. These differences must be noted. The Australian aborigines and the Bushmen would need a good deal of education before they could run a country as well as the Danes or Swiss run theirs. The English people do not in general show an equally fine artistic sense and taste as the Italian or the French. These differences affect economic activities.

And here the economist steps in. All this time I have been trying to keep him out by denying that there is such a subject as economic geography, and by constantly emphasising non-material factors, but at last I must admit that the economist has a good deal to say. Even when sweethearting, honeyed words are not enough: sometimes chocolates or a good meal will convey more to the loved one. I have already mentioned that one needs to know something of economics and the essence of pure economics is the theory of value. Geographers are too prone to speak of men producing goods of whatsoever kind rather like bees produce honey or spiders produce the gossamer filament from their toes or whatever part of their anatomy it comes from. Nature herself is not interested in prices, she just produces, but man never does that, he is always calculating. Is it worth while, will it pay? are constant questions which are asked equally by capitalist or communist. We are all asking these questions though we may not do so openly: all the time we are pricing and appraising things. It is only the very wealthy who can afford to ignore costs and prices and even then not for everything. What does it cost? is a most difficult question to answer. Marshall distinguishes between real and money costs. Real costs are all those human efforts, abstinences and sufferings of whatsoever kind which go in producing something: money costs are all the payments made in and during this process of production. They do not necessarily coincide and a great deal of thinking, both good and bad, has been devoted to the subject.

Wheat is grown in East Anglia, in the Prairie Provinces of Canada: cotton is manufactured in Lancashire, but how much is produced or how little will depend upon the price offered and upon the costs of production, and costs of production are only the various prices added together of labour and of implements. It is always a matter of costing and calculation. It must be so even in the so called communist state, everywhere so long as capital is inadequate for all the possible uses to which it can be put. One does not have to study economics for long to realise that these problems of evaluation are terribly difficult to work out, and indeed that people will never wholly agree, simply because most of the starting points from which the discussion begins are merely postulated points. A simple book for beginners, and there are very many, is *Men, Money and Markets* by M. D. R. Leys, Cairncross's *Economics* is more advanced and gives one some of the modern jargon, but the writer still has a real affection for Marshall's *Economics of Industry*. This last book is now regarded by many as dated and out-moded, but for the general reader who wishes to study economics it is still the best. Marshall had a passion for accuracy in words and insisted upon definition, and he had that uncommon combination found in the greater geniuses such as Adam Smith, of having his head in the clouds and his feet firmly on the ground. He's not easy reading.

This study of principles is very necessary, especially today when planning is so widely advocated. Most planning is *ad hoc*, particular problems are taken by themselves and the solution found without any reference to the rest of the surrounding world with disastrous results. The evils of the *ad hoc* legislation in Victorian times is very apparent and none expose it more than the present day planners who are repeating it on a vaster scale. Today we urgently need to search for principles. When we can think clearly, then we can look at the detailed studies. Read Jewkes *Ordeal by Planning* by an acknowledged economist. Even if you are very pink read it for the success of socialism, if it comes, can only come if socialists become self critical instead of emotionally sanctimonious. If you are really red, there is no need to give any advice, as that comes in regular supply from a distant city.

In the chapters which follow, I have tried to deal with certain aspects of our subject, but I have been forced to do things which are in themselves dangerous. For instance, the study of life is essentially a dynamic one: life cannot be static, though the speed at which it is lived and flows will vary from one age to another and from one country to another. If we were searching for static civilisation, one would have pointed to China seventy years ago but one would have been wrong. China was never really static, and certainly seventy years ago forces were being generated which were to disrupt it later. But it is difficult to study anything in motion when beginning, so for teaching purposes we teach as if conditions are static. A dangerous though necessary thing to do. At some time, however, the dynamic approach must be made. Then, too, life is a living whole and will not be divided into compartments. Again for teaching purposes, we begin by pulling the machine to pieces and exhibiting each separate part. This I have done chapter by chapter, but somehow the reader has to imagine all the chapters applying at the same instant. The simile of the machine is a bad one. Life is functional, and so infinitely more complex. Again a reason why the reader should use his imagination. And may I say to the younger readers that a realisation of the functional life of a community is very necessary. When young, one is naturally in a hurry and impatient, and it can be an antidote to some of us elder ones who can be too slow. Age does not bring wisdom only, even when it brings that. Some of us have, however, learnt a few things, and one of them is the fact that human nature changes very slowly and institutional changes should not go more rapidly than moral education, otherwise they lead to violence and chaos.

Before passing to the latter part of this chapter I would suggest a few books. For the beginner there is a Penguin, *The World's Wealth* by W. G. Moore which is a readable introduction, Dudley Stamp's *Intermediate Commercial Geography* is a good text book. The first volume deals with commodities, regions, and world trade: the second with countries. This gives a brief reminder of the regional background and has very useful maps. For more advanced readers E. W. Zimmerman's *World Resources and Industries*, Bengston and van Royen *Fundamentals of Economic Geography* are both very good. They cover a good deal of the same ground and there is no reason to read all of both. Finally, *An Introduction to World Economics* by E. M. Patterson should be known to advanced students. There is a mass of fact in all these books and they are well written.

In this latter portion of the chapter I wish to discuss the important matter of definition and meaning of terms. The reader will find that I have stopped from time to time for explanation and definition, but nevertheless it is worth while considering the matter a little more fully.

We can only think accurately through language, though language itself has distinct limitations, but for the moment we are concerned with making the best of what we have.

All science and scientific thinking premises accuracy of measurement and accuracy in the use and meaning of words and expressions. That is why the physical sciences have invented words of their own, so that when a word is used everyone knows exactly what is meant, whereas in ordinary speech words are used very loosely. It is this looseness which makes general conversation easy, as nobody really knows what he or she is talking about, and that is why the scientist can be such a bore in general company. We as scientists ought to aim at strict accuracy of meaning when on duty, and when we cannot agree, as do the physical scientists, to make a jargon we should at least define our terms so that the listener or reader knows what we mean. Take a simple example in which the writer was once trapped. The word 'gentleman', a word much sniffed at these democratic days but which is commonly used and misused in spite of that fact. When walking with a German and a Frenchman in one's youth, the conversation turned on to the difficulties of exact translation from one language to another. Certain words and phrases, as the reader will know, just can't be accurately translated. I was asked to define the word 'gentleman' which I proceeded to do, but as I went on I got more and more involved, what with the German methodical mind and the French quick and penetrating one. Finally the Frenchman said, 'And would you in the light of your definition call your king a gentleman?' It was checkmate. Today I know where I went wrong. Or shall we take a statement made in a student's debate on the study of the classics slightly more than forty years ago, 'No man can be a gentleman who has not studied both Latin and Greek'. How relieved one felt to have qualified for I had done three months' Greek! Is one a gentleman today when that very slight tincture of Greek has wholly evaporated? Nevertheless the word has a core of meaning which will not be denied. Bernard Shaw's demand for a new political dictionary would not solve any of our problems as people will allow their emotions to dominate their words. One can call an intimate friend a fool, but might hesitate to call an acquaintance one, while to so call a complete stranger is asking for trouble. One can say things which have completely different meanings, according to the tone of the voice or the expression of one's face, though the words remain exactly the same. That is one of the many reasons why it is so difficult to judge between people in a quarrel. All this is the stuff which makes life both inter-esting and difficult, but the scientist must have a dictionary. Bernard Shaw's dictionary pre-supposes that politicians and statesmen are dispassionate scientists which even he doesn't believe. Anyhow not many scientists are as dispassionate as one would wish.

The economists had to face this problem, and tried to com-promise with not too happy results, though of late years they have been building up a jargon of their own. Let us take three apparently simple terms: necessaries, comforts and luxuries. The modern enlightened world demands that wages shall be sufficient to provide at least the necessaries of life to all, and, if possible, some of the comforts. Here is something upon which we all agree until we begin to translate the terms into actual meaning. Let the reader and some friends discuss these terms and see how far they agree. The economists have divided necessaries into necessaries for existence, conventional neces-saries and necessaries for efficiency. That sounds better, but is it? Is a fur coat a necessity? Most husbands think not, and may-be some wives. So one can go on. It would seem that such terms must be discussed with reference to time, place and pre-vailing conditions. Thus a fur coat may be deemed a comfort or a luxury in this country, but a necessity in a Russian or Canadian winter. Then of course, there is fur and fur, ranging from dishonest rabbit skin, to honest mink. We today with our advanced techniques and productive powers and our ideas of living have raised our standards and so define necessaries in a different way from our ancestors. Today we consider a bathroom in a working man's house a necessity. Certainly my grandparents did not and there wasn't one in my lodgings when I was an undergraduate. Diogenes did not think washing was a necessity, and only recently a graduate in philosophy of one of the older universities laid it down quite definitely that modern cleanliness was unnecessary, and one's nose confirmed the speaker's asseveration. Smoking has become what? a necessity, a conventional necessary, a comfort or a luxury? This is important to many of my readers, though not to me, for if it is a luxury the planners may do away with it as it sounds plutocratic; if a comfort, then because it is bourgeois, if a conventional necessary, this can be modified by a wise and all-directing state which knows all about the art of conditioning. Perhaps it is a necessary for existence. Certainly it is for the existence of any government in this country which would be voted out at once if smoking were prohibited. Such definitions must be arbitrary, and if so, each person has a right to his own interpretation, though he must make himself explicit.

Much or all of our statistical data has meaning only when we know what are the definitions behind the figures. The degree of urbanisation depends upon the definition of what constitutes a town. I have dealt with this elsewhere. Crime figures are very much a matter of definition. Crime increased alarmingly when the law forbade the leaving of cars just anywhere instead of at appointed places. The amount of undetected crime today must be even more alarming with all the present laws which direct and misdirect our lives. Which of my readers is not a criminal? Unemployment figures are very much a matter of definition, thus we can decrease unemployment by lowering the age for retirement and old age pensions. Unemployment figures often fail to reveal disguised unemployment. One ought never just to take figures and use them without asking what are the definitions. The Disarmaments Conference between the wars broke down partly because no one could define what constituted a soldier. Let the reader ask himself this important question and he will see some of the difficulties.

There are all sorts of terms used with reference to land classification, desert, steppe-desert, temperate grass-lands. What exactly constitutes a desert? Is it a place wholly devoid of vegetation and so of human and animal life. Even the Rab al Khali does not fulfil that strict condition, and even when such terms have been defined with the requisite elasticity the marginal areas still remain. If then such regions have to be measured and the figures recorded we must know how it was done. How much of the earth's surface is still available for settlement and capable of cultivation? Figures in such an investigation have no meaning without rigid definition, "Baker estimates the desert area of the world at about 15·6 million square miles; Thronthwaite at about 8·5 million". It doesn't matter for the moment who Baker and Thornthwaite may be, but it does matter that the figures differ so greatly. Actually, when one inquires one finds the difference is mostly due to definition. Again we are told that there are in the world about 30 million square miles sufficiently warm and wet for agriculture, but again we have been told nothing. Agriculture may mean anything from the best type of farming we know in such a country as our own to the very marginal farms in Australia or the semi-arid and poverty-stricken peasant holdings in Kansu.

Fertile land may mean many things. David Ricardo who did so much damage to this country in the early nineteenth century talked about fertility as if it were absolute instead of relative. He also wrote about the 'original and indestructible properties' of the soil, but he was a townsman, born and bred, who made his fortune on the Stock Exchange and a brilliant abstract thinker. A farmer could have told him a few things and so could some of the children down the coal-mines. Abstract thinkers need to be carefully watched and controlled. There aren't many 'original' and certainly no 'indestructible' properties as they found out in the 'Dust bowl' when the soil just blew away. The term fertility must be used with reference to the kind of crop, the rotation employed and the whole art and lay-out of agriculture. Here is a piece of arid steppe-desert which will nourish a few camels and a few miserable goats yet put water on it and it will blossom like the rose. Here are pestilential swamps which, if drained, will support a dense population, or again much land lacks fertility merely because some one chemical substance is wanting. So too words such as waste, rough grazing, cultivable land are just words and nothing more. In all these studies the student must go and see. No reading of books, statistics or of definitions will suffice. It is like trying to tell a person born blind what blue looks like. The real things in life must be experienced to be known. Books by themselves are desperately dangerous things.

When is a country empty, full or over-crowded? What do we mean by an optimum population? Words again. The nearest approach to an empty land is the Antarctic, but that gets us nowhere. It is often asserted that the crowded and congested lands should send their surplus to the empty lands. It sounds reasonable and easy but it is not quite easy, and often not very reasonable. Take a case. Australia, it is alleged, is relatively empty. Empty relatively to what? How many people will Australia hold? Nobody has answered that question yet. Griffith Taylor has a chapter on this in his book *Australia*. He suggests 30 millions: others say more and no doubt the Chinese and Japanese could pack in more than we Europeans. It will depend partly upon the amount of land available for use, and this brings us back to the difficulties we have already glanced at. Then if we are speaking of filling up empty lands we should allow for time. Given a couple of centuries, the Australians at the present rate of growth will fill up their country quite nicely. Must they have it filled within the next ten years? There is only one reason for haste, and that is fear of invasion. I have dealt elsewhere with migration.

Let us now turn to industry. One notes at once that the word has a broad and a narrow use. Agriculture, mining and fishing are industries, and when one is listing the industries of a country one includes every kind of occupation. In the narrow sense the word often means manufacturing industry and one thinks of modern factories and works, but domestic and hand industries should be included. Sometimes the change in extension of meaning is obvious, and the reader can be left to pick it up, but often there is ambiguity and one should be at pains to make oneself clear.

A much used and abused term is 'mass production'. We are prone to use the word mass a good deal these days, we speak of the masses, of mass observation and of mass unemployment. It is a dangerous word at the best and a nasty and humiliating one ordinarily. The 'masses' have obviously lost their individuality and their humanity. They are no longer human and perhaps that is why they must be chivvied about so much. But to return to the term mass production, which only came into common use between the wars. Does it mean producing on a large scale? for Lancashire was evidently mass producing cloth long ago. How much production is necessary to constitute 'mass' production? It is a term which seems to have crept in with the automobile and lighter engineering trades which have employed an ultra-minute division of labour and then grouped their labour along a moving belt. If, however, one means large scale production the old term is still quite useful. The term, mass production, has, however, an hypnotic effect upon most people who can see the world's troubles almost automatically solved by merely murmuring the magic word. We would be wise to keep our senses. In a proper world there is place for large scale and small scale production, and there are limits to the alleged economies of mass production, quite apart from the human and social limits which are much more marked.

Then, because manufacturing industry is so diverse that we cannot grasp its endless variety, we tend to simplify our thinking by the use of blanket terms such as the 'iron and steel industry', 'the engineering industry', 'the chemical industry'. Let us take the 'iron and steel' as an example. The Survey of Metal Industries (Part IV)[1] defines this industry, "as including the smelting of iron ore: the conversion of the pig-iron so obtained into wrought iron and into steel; the casting, rolling or forging

[1] Committee on Industry and Trade, 1928.

of iron and steel; and the manufacture of more highly finished products such as galvanised sheets, tinplates, wire and wire manufactures, nails and screws, bolts and nuts, anchors and chains, bedsteads and hollow ware. There is no clear-cut distinction between the iron and steel industries and the engineering industries and the above delimitation is, therefore, arbitrary." It gives a diagram showing the relationships. The whole chapter is well worth reading. The Report of the Import Duties Advisory Committee of 1937[1] in its definition largely agrees with this and criticises the Board of Trade Census of Production, which includes not only all in the above definition but also metallic furniture, tools and implements, cutlery, needles, pins and metallic smallwares and also small arms. If then one is examining statistics how can one possibly make sense of them unless all the definitions are clearly stated and tally? It is the elasticity in definition which accounts for so many apparent discrepancies found in them. Now and then one ought to be supplied with complete detailed lists of goods manufactured. This is the more necessary today because planning always likes to make things neat and tidy. This is possible on paper but life itself will never permit itself to be so brushed and combed.

Then there is that great miscellaneous assortment of industries which defies classification, but which is often lumped together as 'secondary industry' or 'light industries'. 'Secondary industry', as a term seems to have a slightly derogatory sense. It is not so vital and important as the primary or basic industries, but that all depends upon what you want or what you think is right and proper. For instance, the iron and steel and the engineering industries take pride of place. They are the foundations upon which we build. Contrast that with a factory turning out potato-crisps or even the little industry which makes artificial eyelashes and finger-nails. Here is dignity and impudence: virtue and vice. Of course these heavy industries are vital, and it is doubtful if many will approve of the last, but in a free society there it is. There is another term 'a free society' which I will leave as a suggestion to the reader for a full evening's entertainment with his friends. That brings one to the difficult

Cmd. 5507.

and delicate business of the consumers' choice.   There used to
be a slogan, 'The customer is always right' which, like most
slogans, was not wholly true.   The customer can be very wrong
at times, as when he wants 'white snow' in large quantities,
but he is not always and wholly wrong in some of his wants.
Where secondary industry begins and ends is a purely arbitrary
decision.   These terms are useful as a kind of shorthand allusion
but nothing more.

There are certain geographical expressions against which
one should be on one's guard.   We all know or should know
very clearly what particular piece of territory we are talking
about when we mention France.   We used to know once upon
a time what we meant by the United Kingdom, but have been in
doubt until very recently when the matter has been settled.   The
British Empire is another difficult term.   Both these expressions
must be clarified when one is making quantitative comparisons
over considerable periods of time.   So with Germany and the
U.S.S.R.   Statistics are not comparable when studying such
entities at such different dates as 1914, 1924, and 1948.   So in
future it will be more difficult to speak of India which now
means the Dominion of India, and geographers will have to be
careful to say exactly what they mean.   But there are other terms
commonly used which are much more vague, such as Central
Asia, the Middle East, the Near East.   One notices, if watching
the development of geographical knowledge, that as our knowledge becomes more precise so these terms tend to disappear,
at least among geographers, though politicians and journalists
like them as it does not tie them down, and they can mislead
themselves and everybody else very happily.   Such vague
terms are a sure sign of a vague knowledge.   Let us discuss
them very briefly.

The Middle East will certainly comprise Iran and Iraq.
Does it include Palestine and Syria?   Years ago when the
Turkish Empire was still in existence these were included in
the Near East, but the Near East seems to have disappeared with
the Turkish Empire.   Egypt is now generally thought of as
Egypt.   At one time it was part of the Near East.   Arabia
presents a problem.   Is it to be included in the Middle East

B

or not.   Perhaps Arabia is better left as Arabia: it is a pretty clear cut definition and area.   If then we throw in Syria and Palestine into the Middle East there we are with four political areas.   Turkey today is just Turkey.   Not everyone would agree with this analysis, but at least the reader knows what I am talking about when I allude to the Middle East.

Central Asia is even more delightfully vague and one can see the caravans dimly through the . heat haze and the dust while Golden Samarkand is somewhere beyond the mirage. But we geographers must get the dust out of our eyes and see clearly.   Let us approach the definition negatively and say what it does not include.   That by the way can be a useful method of attacking some problems.   It does not include the peripheral countries of Afghanistan, India, China, Manchuria, Siberia. That leaves what is practically the desert or steppe-desert portion of Asia which fans out from the Pamirs and includes Russian and Chinese Turkestan, the Mongolias and Tibet.   One might be inclined to exclude Russian Turkestan which has now been integrated into the U.S.S.R. and we might be doubtful about Outer Mongolia, which, though claimed as a Chinese sphere of influence, is certainly within the Russian fold at the moment. So we can make a choice of either the broader definition which is certainly useful for some purposes, or the narrower one. Again it doesn't matter so long as one is quite explicit.   It's rather like the above mentioned definition of a gentleman according to the classics enthusiast.   If you haven't studied Greek you've just had it.   So here it is an equally arbitrary matter within reason.   Again it may be said that these expressions, too, are useful shorthand provided you know that is all they are meant for, and for precise thinking name your countries accurately.

There is one final matter when talking of definition.   When speaking of peoples call them by their proper designations. If you are English don't insult a Scot or an Irishman by extending the term to them.   The Welsh take it more quietly, but some get uneasy.   Remember the English are not the most popular people in the world.   This is a surprise to some.   When speaking of other races such as Africans or Asiatics, they too are better alluded to by their correct names. The term Indian for instance has as much meaning as that of European. No one thinks that a Spaniard is like a Norwegian or a Dane like a Greek. So with Indians, they are equally diverse and numerous; Bengalis, Tamils, Bhils, Marathas and so on. Africans break up into equally distinct peoples. And never use the word native if you can avoid it as it has a bad meaning and what is worse it stops you thinking. There is a proper use of the word when it would be equally applicable to black, brown, yellow or white. Sometimes reference has to be made to colour as when discussing the colour clashes in certain parts of the world.

CHAPTER II

FACTS AND STATISTICS

Facts in themselves are mere dry bones, dull things of little value until they have been so clothed with reality that they become living things. That is why the man who always insists upon 'facts' is such a bore and menace to the truth. Of what value is the date 1066 which most of us know so well that we have fled from it by turning it into a joke. Most people's reflexes would respond: 1066—Battle of Hastings, and then cease. Who, however, is interested in a dog fight between Saxons and Normans? We have had too many of our own to be impressed. If, however, this battle, which was not fought at Hastings, marks for us the intrusion of a new people, a new culture out of which the English people sprang, then it becomes interesting. It is not the battle that matters but the coming of the Normans with their superior civilisation. It is like being born. One does not need a birth certificate to prove that. One is one's own birth certificate. Only a civil servant or a lawyer needs a certificate to prove we are born when talking to us, but if it be a case of identity, of an inheritance, then a certificate may be useful and necessary. Facts are useful landmarks which prevent the imagination having too much play, and the human race are too much given to letting their imaginations run away with them when their emotions are at work, which they generally are. Most ghost stories are based upon imagination. And here may I recommend M. R. James' *Collected Ghost Stories*. These are the best ever written and should be read by candlelight preferably when alone in the house. The story, "Oh, whistle, and I'll come to you, my lad," is the perfect example of how not to be a scientist. Most propaganda is imagination without facts, or imagination distorting facts.

The economic geographer is not very interested in facts as such, but only as they help him to interpret tendencies. What is the present coal position? Are we short of food or not? Such questions demand facts to answer them. We shall need to know how much coal is being produced today. That can be ascertained but can be misleading, because 'coal' is a fact which needs much elaborating. There are many kinds and qualities. Actually it is calorific quality which largely matters, though that may not be all. Thus not all coal is good for coking for blast furnaces purposes. Japanese coal is not. Durham coal is particularly well suited to this purpose. The surface mining which has been developed the last few years produces 'coal', but of very poor quality. Then having estimated the output of coal one must estimate the demand. It is well to remember that an estimate is an estimate: it is not a fact. I may think the moon is made of green cheese but that is not a fact. A government official may decide that the nation is adequately fed on the present balanced diet but some of us know better. The government-paid experts say 'yes' but our stomachs and lack of vigour say 'no'. Maybe the government is right, maybe not.

We shall have something to say about patterns of industry and such patterns cannot be known except through facts. So facts we shall need to know. That raises a difficult point which ought to be settled. The geographer deals with facts as they are now in the present. But what do we mean by the present? Today, we may reply. But surely this is inaccurate. I have had my breakfast so that is the past. I hope to have my lunch so that is the future. Thus we can narrow down the present to a fine point which divides the past from the future. Actually in our thoughts we are living largely in the immediate past and the immediate future. This, very inaccurately, we call the present. The present is something we can watch, in which we are either an actor or spectator or both and so we blur past and present. Suppose you are faced with the question: describe the position of English farming today. Your survey will of necessity take you some way into the immediate past and immediate future. You cannot avoid it. One notices, however, how much economic activity is concerned with the future. All our activities are based upon estimates of future wants. That is why a relatively stable world is so desirable. We can forecast the future only by projecting the curves of the past and present. Such projections must be contingent upon conditions remaining much the same. A ration state for an infantry battalion in peace manoeuvres can be sent in and acted upon with complete confidence. At the most there will be only one or two casualties, but a ration state for a battalion going into action is a very problematical affair. "The Economic Survey for 1948" does not deal with facts though they may look like it when set out and printed. It deals with estimates. Estimates should be based upon facts, but the further the estimates reach out into the future the less reliable they become, especially in a changing world. That is why so much of the present estimating, whether by our own planners or by those who are trying to put the world right, goes astray. But given our type of world, estimates we must have and these must be based upon facts. The time element is important in all this estimating, and I would recommend all students to be constantly aware of it. One can take the present as meaning today or this week or this present year. The future may be divided purely for convenience into the near future of, say, the next few years: the more distant future of ten to fifteen years, the still more distant future of twenty to twenty-five years. There is no point in reaching further forward. The world is changing so rapidly that we cannot premise lasting conditions. We are forecasting and estimating, not prophesying.

However we allow for time we should be clear in our minds what exactly we mean and should make it perfectly clear to others. It is important not to change the length of a period unconsciously. Much bad thinking arises from this and still more when others are not informed. Economists often talk of long and short periods. A short period is one in which there is not enough time to adjust supply to demand: a long period one in which there is. To beginners time periods are thought of as separate things but actually they should be thought of as functioning at the same time, sometimes reinforcing each other: often in antagonism. Many of the present day problems arise out of this conflict between the immediate and the future. Wise policies must allow for both, if they do not you may notice that though the operation has been successful the patient dies. Facts can be obtained if one knows where to look for them, and it is obviously absurd to try to memorise not only because of the vastness of the field of study but because the facts themselves are changing all the time. What we need to know is where to look and how to use what we find. Of course the more facts we have in our heads the better. It saves time looking them up, and in examination rooms where unhappily reference books are not yet allowed we must have some. We cannot reason in a vacuum. But the mere memorising of facts is to be depreciated. Given the proper approach and a real interest the facts largely remember themselves. It is rather like the small boy remembering cricket averages when he can never learn his dates in history. He remembers what interests him. This, however, is not the whole theory of education.

What we want to do is to learn (1) where to look for our data, and (2) how to interpret and use it when obtained. The nature of the data will depend upon the breadth and depth of the study. Those who are beginning the study of Economic Geography, which will most probably be one among several subjects, cannot be expected to have either the time or experience to look for their facts as would more advanced students, nor will these have the same need or opportunities as one who is doing real research work on a definitely defined subject. Beginners, therefore, can be referred to a few sources such as Year Books and Statistical Abstracts. It is as well to know to some slight extent what data are available.

Modern governments publish large quantities of statistics and reports, though these are seldom compiled merely for the convenience of economic geographers. These are the main sources of our raw material. With the more advanced countries the primary difficulty lies in the apparent excess of material, though when one is making any detailed research one finds that there is nearly always a lack of material or at least of the right kind of material. Most of this material is pure statistics but much and the more useful for our present purpose is accompanied by explanatory and descriptive matter. Naturally each country publishes in its own language, no great hindrance when it is merely a matter of translating headings. A dictionary will suffice. But where there is typescript a knowledge of some languages is useful.

For general purposes and for the student one can and must reduce the range of these sources very considerably. No harm is done provided always that one remembers that the pruning has been done and that the conclusions drawn must be conditioned by this limitation. Here then are some of our sources:

I. Statistical Abstracts: Most countries publish these though they are not always easily available and may be expensive. As examples one may mention the Annual Abstract of Statistics for the United Kingdom, The Statistical Abstract for the U.S.A., the Annuaire Statistique for France.

These, as the titles imply, are abstracts from the larger returns and reports. They cover a very wide range of subjects and so contain a mass of data which we shall not want. They are purely statistical and very condensed. Those who do not like figures in the mass will be repelled by them, but one soon begins to find one's way about. They are not really more complex than the London Underground. The thing to do is to ignore and not see the figures one does not need.

II. Various Year Books and Handbooks published by most governments. These generally contain a very considerable amount of printed matter and are exceedingly useful particularly to the beginner and to the student. They have the advantage of being relatively cheap. Nearly all have special articles so that one can often refer back to past numbers for information. All have maps and diagrams: a few from the more artistic nations have delightful sketches and drawings. All the British Dominions publish these though there never was one for India. The U.S.A. Agriculture Year Books fall into this group. Excellent books and mines of information. Some with special names such as "Soils and Men";

"Climate" are invaluable. The *Brazilian Year Book* is excellent both for its facts and as an artistic production. The *Japanese Year Book*, in English, is also excellent.

III. Government Reports of various kinds. These may be routine reports published periodically or may be special reports appearing from time to time or for some special reason. All countries publish these in very considerable numbers. A few dealing with Great Britain and the Empire will be mentioned as types of what appear elsewhere.

The Report of the Committee on Industry and Trade. Generally known as the Balfour Reports after the Chairman. These were published between 1927–29 in six volumes. In their time they supplied us geographers with a mass of data. We badly need a similar kind of inquiry today as at the moment no one knows where they are or anything is.

The Working Party Reports of which there are several. Those in the Cotton and Wool Industries are good examples.

Distribution of Industry. Cmd. 7540, 1948.

The Report on the Coal Industry 1925 which supplies a view of the Coal Industry.

The Report on Indian Agriculture generally known as the Linlithgow Report 1928. It is by no means out of date. India moves slowly especially in the countryside. There is an 'abridged report' of some 80 pages. This is good but better after one has read the larger report. All small books are good after one has read the large ones.

The Final Report of the Drought Investigation Commission (South Africa) 1932. A very impressive and illuminating report which still applies. It deals with the causes of erosion, a subject very much to the fore these days. Unfortunately, it is out of print and practically impossible to obtain. There are a few copies in libraries such as South Africa House.

The Third Interim Report of the Industrial and Agri-

B*

cultural Requirements Commisson: South Africa V.G. '40–'41.

Investigation into Manufacturing Industries in the Union of South Africa 1945.

Report of the Advisory Committee . . . in the Iron and Steel Industry: Cmd. 5507 of 1937.

Iron and Steel Industry Reports by the British Iron and Steel Federation and the Joint Iron Council: Cmd. 6811 of 1946.

These publications are fairly expensive, and students could not be expected to buy them. But they can be found in the better equipped libraries.

IV. Trade Reports of all kinds such as those issued by the late Department of Overseas Trade now merged into a new series published by the Export Promotion Department of the Board of Trade.

These vary very greatly in quality and usefulness. Now and then a special number would be issued such as No 851 of 1934 on the Economic Condition of France: or No. 641 of 1936 on Germany, which were and are invaluable, but mostly the reports are of medium value.

The new series are excellent and particularly useful as they give a summary for the past nine years. They contain a great deal of very useful stuff very well set out.

The new series of Colonial Annual Reports published by the Colonial Office. As former publications ceased in 1940 they give a general résumé bringing one up to date. This new series is excellently produced with good illustrations. The Colonial Office also publish reports on the Mandated Territories and these too are excellent. These all contain, as do the other reports, much one does not need so that one must learn to pick out what one does need.

V. Annuals and Year Books mostly non-governmental such as:

1. The *Statesman's Year Book*. This contains a mass of information which does not greatly interest us.

The figures are too compressed to be useful. One has to remember that compression in statistics can go too far. The figures in themselves may be correct but can only be read correctly if one knows the method by which they are obtained. One does not recommend it to the beginner or very much to anyone.

2. The *International Year Book of Agricultural Statistics*, commonly known as the " Rome Year Book." This gives data for the whole world and in its way is authoritative. It too suffers from compression though of a different kind. It is impossible to put our very diversified world into the strait waistcoat of a questionnaire, however well devised. One must use this Year Book for more advanced work, but like any other statistical work it is only really useful when one knows how it has been compiled.

3. The *International Statistical Year Book of Geneva*. Very useful, and one must go to it constantly especially if in a hurry, but the same applies to it as was said of the " Rome Year Book."

4. *The Mineral Industry* published by the McGraw-Hill Book Company, U.S.A. A most excellent work concerning the whole world. The Americans are especially good on this kind of work.

The above have been chosen merely as types of publications which can be found in all languages and which are published by all modern countries. They are too numerous and too detailed for use by the beginner, though as he progresses he will come to them more and more. But even the beginner should know where we get our stuff. There used to be published annually a Guide to Current Official Statistics of the U.K. This ceased during the War, but today there appears the Government Publications Consolidated List for one shilling. It is a most interesting and exciting catalogue and may snare one into reading all kinds of reports. There is also a monthly list.

In addition to the above there are books dealing with specific problems and which are constantly appearing.

In handling data of any kind it is imperative that we should have some knowledge of how it is compiled and the method of handling and dealing with the figures collected. The more one knows of statistics the better, but it is not necessary that a beginner should understand the technique in detail, only that he should be aware that 'simple facts' are rarely simple and often very complex. It is not so much the techniques of computation as the nature of the background from which the collection is made. For those who so desire one recommends such books as Holman (L. J.) *Simplified Statistics* or Tippet (L. H. C.) *Statistics*. But if the formulae confuse, leave them.

In addition to this technical knowledge it is very desirable in any real study that we should have some personal knowledge of the country and industry to which the figures relate. This seems a counsel of perfection as indeed it is. Not many of us can go touring the world, nor can one make a detailed study of even one foreign country on £35, but it is possible to study a region in one's own country. Study the spread of the industries great and small. Visit the factories, if possible. It all helps. There is, however, no doubt that living abroad is necessary for a thorough understanding. One should live and work there as only in that way does one get to know a country and its people. Tourists learn nothing, or generally the wrong things, and soldiers haven't time for economics. If one cannot travel, then one should insist that the books one reads are written by those who have. From this it follows that no one can write authoritative books on economic geography for the whole world. Such books must be largely compilations. They have their use but should be used with great care and even distrust.

Facts and statistics must never be torn out of their settings and used outside the specified conditions. Statistics never lie unless they are made to do so by either the dishonest or the ignorant. It is hard to know which person does the greatest harm, though probably the latter. Let us take a case of honest ignorance—a statement made in a book written by a visitor to India. This statement was made as a basis of an argument which does not concern us here. It was that the population of India had increased 55% between 1872 and 1921. If we check up in the Statistical Abstract we find that the figures are:

1872	206,162,000
1881	253,896,000
1891	287,315,000
1901	294,361,000
1911	315,156,000
1921	318,942,000

That is, they verify the statement.   But if we go to the Census reports from which the Abstract was made we find an interesting number of things.   First, the figure for 1872 is not a firm figure but only an estimate.   It might well have been 10 or 20 million more.   Estimates of this kind are subject to very considerable margins of error.   The first synchronous census was taken only in 1881.   Secondly, new areas were included in the later censuses and these accounted for 43·3 million in the increase.   Thirdly, improved methods of counting accounted for 15·7 million. It is not easy to count a vast population in a great country like India.   The real increase was actually 53·8 million, slightly less than half the nominal total.   The argument which followed was of no value as it was based upon an inaccurate figure.

Period	Increase due to Inclusion of new areas	Increase due to Improved method	Real Increase	Total	Rate % of real increase	Period
1872–81	33	12	3	48	1·5	1872–81
1881–91	5·7	3·5	24·3	33·5	9·6	1881–91
1891–01	2·7	·2	4·1	7·0	1·4	1891–01
1901–11	1·8		18·	20·5	6·4	1901–11
1911–21	·1		3·77	3·8	1·2	1911–21
Total	43·3	15·7	53·8	112·8	20·1	

Let us consider by way of example a few simple cases.   One of the first things we should do as geographers when approaching the study of any country is to ask its size as this, other things being equal, is important not only from the population point of view but from that of its general productivity. Thus, if one is comparing the U.S.A. with the U.K., as a producer of, say, raw materials, it does matter that the U.S. has an area of over 3,000,000 sq. miles not including Alaska, and that the British Isles are 121,000. The U.S. coalfields cover a far greater extent than the whole of this country. But something more than the bare figure is required. One needs to know how much is available for each purpose. As geographers we divide countries into regions—desert, steppe-desert, semi-arid, etc. All this we should require to know. Yet where does the desert end and the steppe-desert begin? These divisions must be arbitrary and one will note that when such statistics are being compiled the experts differ greatly. What is cultivable land? We will ask that question again, but there can be no final answer. All such definitions must also be arbitrary so they should be made known. It does not matter so much whether the definition is broader or narrower, but it does matter that it should be known to all. It will quite often happen then that figures which look final in print are quite inaccurate and misleading. One ought to be somewhat sceptical of potted statistics. If our study takes us over a considerable period of time such as a generation or half a century it is very necessary to know if we are considering the same unit. Thus Germany was enlarged by the annexation of Alsace-Lorraine after the Franco-Prussian war. This was lost after the Great War. Later Nazi Germany was enlarged by the annexation of Austria and Czecho-Slovakia. The foreign trade figures for India were affected when Burma was separated from India in 1934. Some books, for instance, used to mention India as an exporter of rice. Politically this was accurate until Burma was separated: economically it never was. India has been a net importer of rice for some years. Again the trade figures for our own country were affected when Eire became an independent Dominion. It affected many of the figures for the United Kingdom, which had now shrunk in size and population. One must take care particularly with the agricultural returns.

Finally, let us consider certain figures which as economic geographers we need at the beginning of the study of any country. How many people are employed and in what occupations? You will notice that most geography books only refer to certain types of industry. If, for instance, we take Great Britain we will think at once of agriculture, mining, fishing, iron and steel, engineering, electrical, chemical and, say, the textiles. These do employ great numbers but they are by no means inclusive. Moreover, most of the terms are vague and need to be broken down into something more definite.

A brief analysis of the occupations of the country can be found in the Annual Abstract for 1935046 (No. 84), pages 15 and 16. These are for England, Wales and Scotland only. North Ireland is excluded. The figures are for 1911, 1921 and 1931. The first thing is to notice the total numbers employed which will increase not only as population grows but as the higher age groups increase relatively to the lower ones. There are fewer children these days. Four great occupations stand out— agriculture, mining, metals, and transport, each with over 1,000,000. But personal service, including hotels, accounts for 2,405,000. Textile and clothing accounts for 850,000, which is 200,000 less than ten years previously. Central and local government and defence took 1,477,000 and we know that today they take a much greater number. Today the Civil Service has some 660,000 more than in 1939: the armed forces too are larger. So we go down the list. This list is very compressed but useful for a quick glance. The P.E.P. Report on Location of Industry has an elaborate analysis which is further divided into regions. It is too elaborate for the beginner. Personally, I prefer the analysis published in the *Ministry of Labour Gazette* for August 1934, p. 268, which gives England and Wales, and for June, p. 198, for Scotland. These numbers, by the way, do not agree with those in the other tables as each set has been modified for various reasons. There is a near enough coincidence for our purpose. The Gazette List for England and Wales gives 32 major headings, and one can learn a great deal by scanning it. For instance, No. 19 is Painters and Decorators, which employed 261,000 men and 36,000 women. Quite an industry. No. 17, Printers and Photographers, 152,000 men and 38,000 women. No. 31, Other and Undefined Workers number 1,667,000 with another 33,000 in Scotland. This group could be broken down into a vast number of trades, and if one were to turn to the full Census returns one could get the details. It is a good illustration of the difficulty in presenting statistics. To most people the table is long and detailed. Actually it is very compressed.

The pre-Adam Smith economists, the Physiocrats, used to distinguish between productive and non-productive workers. Roughly a productive worker was one such as the farmer, the craftsmen who produced foodstuffs and raw materials or who transformed these into consumers' goods. The rest of the people were unproductive. They produced nothing and lived upon the others. The implication seemed to be that they were parasites. Thus a doctor, a teacher, a violinist, a transport worker were non-productive. Later economic analysis abolished this distinction. It was argued that man does not produce any material: all he does is to create utilities, form, place and time. The analysis was logically sound, for the old division got one into logical troubles. Thus the craftsman who made a violin was productive: the man who played it was not. Here was a dilemma, as it could be argued that the man who produced a thing which was put to unproductive use was really doing unproductive work. But the Physiocrats had a reason for their division and we are finding it out today. It was this. In their world all work was done by men's efforts helped somewhat by that of animals, and a very little by Nature turning windmills and blowing ships along. The result was that production was strictly limited. How much farming would we get done in this country if the farmers had the implements and power of 1750? Output was very slight. If, therefore, there were more than a limited number of unproductive workers, whether doctors, fiddlers or civil servants, foodstuffs, raw materials and products thereof would be scarce, or to use a term disapproved of by *The Times*, in short supply. They could not afford the luxury of too many non-productive workers. So with us, today. We have diverted vast numbers of people from 'productive' to 'non-productive' work. There are limits as to how far one can go even in our world with its power-driven machines. These analyses are very important, not only to us geographers, but to the planners. In the former world the relationship between industries and their demands for labour and raw materials was controlled and adjusted through price. Today the price control no longer functions, and we have not yet learned to regulate supplies so as to correlate them with demand. Price is by far the best way of control and regulation in a society where incomes are not too different, but we cannot agree that it was ideal. At present we are living in a world of compromise and finding things difficult. These analyses are, however, merely a beginning as they have told us nothing of the age make-up of the various groups and nothing of the equipment with which they work. Men can produce only very limited amounts with their own muscles, that is why peasant agriculture and craftsman production are so limited. That is why we need to enquire into the amount of power used per worker and into the type of machine and tool to which the power is applied. It does, nevertheless, start us off on our inquiry. What we need, of course, is a new Census of Production. So much has happened since the last was taken. The figures can only be used as a very rough indication of the industrial distribution of labour. They are really more use in teaching us how to handle our facts than as facts themselves.

CHAPTER III

SIZE, GROWTH AND DISTRIBUTION
OF POPULATIONS

IT is obvious that as all economic activity has meaning only
in relation to the human factor, one is compelled sooner or
later to study the size, growth and distribution of populations.
A considerable amount of attention has been paid between the
two wars to the problems of population, partly for purely
economic reasons, partly for others.

The first great writer on the subject was Robert Malthus,
who published his Essay on Population in 1798. He was then
a very young man, a mathematician and a Fellow of Jesus
College, Cambridge. He describes how he came to do it. He
had spent an evening with his father and a friend discussing the
problems of poverty which were forcing themselves on to the
attention of the country. He walked back to his rooms in a
great mental excitement, and as a result wrote his celebrated
essay almost at white heat. It is still worth reading and has all
the interest and attraction of a vivid piece of thinking and
writing. Malthus asserted that population tended to increase
in geometrical progression, i.e. 2, 4, 8, 16, etc., while production
of foodstuffs and raw materials only increased arithmetically,
i.e. 2.4.6.8. etc. From this he drew the conclusion that a time
would arrive for any people, living in a given area and drawing
their sustenance therefrom, when the law of diminishing returns
would act so strongly that production per head would fall and
with it the standard of living. Briefly this law states that additional applications of labour and capital to a given area of land
will, in general, result in an increased output of produce but not
in proportion to the application of labour and capital. It is
this law which is behind the land hunger everywhere. That is
why intensive cultivation has so limited an application. It is,
of course, possible to undercultivate land and it is possible to
introduce totally new techniques, but the tendency to diminish-

ing returns is always there. This fall in per capita production would continue until a new equilibrium was arrived at where the population would live at a low sustenance level. The redundant mouths would be swept away by what he called the positive checks: war, disease, famine and misery. This was the dismal conclusion. The book brought a storm of criticism. Malthus spent the next ten years elaborating his essay and meeting criticism so that the second edition was a documented thesis. In this he had collected all the statistical data he could lay his hands on. Further, he admitted that there was a theoretical escape from this deadly equilibrium. The newly included factor was restraint not only before but after marriage. That he threw it in more as an academic point rather than a practical one does not matter.

In criticising a theory one must be sure of the right approach and must examine the principles involved. If these are sound one can then examine the detail, some of which may be faulty and wrong. If, however, the principles are unsound the whole theory collapses and it is waste of time troubling about detail. What Malthus meant to say can be expressed very briefly. The human race is capable under favourable conditions of doubling its numbers every 25 years, as happened in the New England States in the 18th century. That is, it tends to increase in geometric progression, 1.2.4.8.16, etc. How quickly that procedure can land us into astronomical figures is soon realised. The stories of the smith who shoed the horse, and of the alleged inventor of chess and the Oriental ruler who wished to reward him are all based upon this fact. Further, while it is possible to increase the food supplies in a country by extending the cultivation to new land and by more intensive cultivation, there eventually comes an end to extension and the law of diminishing returns rapidly puts a brake on intensive cultivation. So that however favourably a community may start it will inevitably end by outgrowing its food supplies and by being reduced to starvation if it insists upon a continuously unrestricted birth rate. Take a simple case. Suppose the U.S., which as yet produces a surplus of foodstuffs, which has still much land capable of cultivation and all its land capable of more intensive use, were to double its numbers every 25 years. The present population is roughly 132,000,000: a generation later it would be 264,000,000: then 528,000,000: then 1056,000,000. Need we go on? So far Malthus is correct. His only fault was to try to be too precise in his statement. A common criticism of Malthus is to say that the present population of Great Britain is at least three times what it was when Malthus wrote and that the standard of living is also much higher. But it ignores Malthus' qualifying clause that the community continues to draw its sustenance from the area it inhabits. He made an exception to his general statement in the case of the city-states which drew their supplies from abroad. Malthus could not imagine this country drawing foodstuffs and raw materials from all the world for he wrote in 1789, not very long after Watt had patented his steam engine and when modern transport had not yet been dreamt of. Nor could he imagine the new techniques in agriculture and industry. He was stating a 'pure' case which was misunderstood in its application by those about him and maybe he forgot that fact himself. That populations have not grown in the progression he names is due largely, in the past, to the positive checks which he enumerated—war, disease, famine and misery. These have been the balancers during the past ages and still are in Asia and even in Europe. The recent Bengal famine is a case in point. It has been blamed upon those in control at Calcutta, upon Delhi, but when due allowance is made the truth is that population growth outstrips production. If the death rate in India were suddenly to drop to that of Great Britain it would only be a few years before famine would be widespread. There is a grim comedy in the plans for more sanitary villages and for more hygenic living that ignore production. What India needs is a fall in the birth rate. It should be noted that Western Europe did practice birth control by various methods such as delayed marriage and the pulling down of cottages in this country in the 18th century. That brings us to Malthus' academic point of restraint. As said above he had little belief in it and rightly, but if there cannot be restraint the modern world has techniques for preventing conception. The present low birth rates in Western Europe and the U.S. are due to this. To sum up, given certain techniques of production, any country can hold only a certain number of people living at a given level. Should the techniques improve and/or should new lands be opened up then numbers and standards can advance, but only for a time. Given present techniques the high standards of living in the U.S. are only possible under their conditions: they are not possible in India or China. It does not follow that the U.S. standards are necessary or desirable, but that is not our affair.

This very briefly and roughly is the theory of population. It is not one's purpose here to go into the matter more fully, but readers who so desire can turn first of all to either or both of two small introductory books: *Population* by Harold Wright and another of similar title by Carr-Saunders. These are, however, very elementary. Carr-Saunders *World Population* is fuller and should be read. There are more advanced treatises and monographs dealing with population trends but these become very detailed and imply a knowledge of statistical method which few possess. Anyhow for our present purpose they are beyond our purview. With the books suggested the reader should be able to look at any statistics with enough knowledge to use them with due precaution. He ought to know what is meant by the Gross and Net Reproduction Rates. He ought to know, for instance, that if the net reproductive rate is less than unity, i.e. that if the number of women of childbearing age in the next generation should be smaller than in the present one, then, assuming fertility and mortality rates to remain unchanged, a decline in population will take place in due course. Thus before the war this rate for England and Wales was between ·7 and ·8 and it was generally below unity in most north-western European countries. For the further study of this point Part I of Reddaway's book, *The Economics of a Declining Population*, is very useful and should be read.

The economic geographer must always ask what is the size of the population of the particular country he is studying. But he must ask a good deal more. It is necessary to know what the numbers have been during the past half century at least, and the rates of growth must be noted. All this is best seen graphically and curves should be studied. Some people don't like curves just as many cannot follow mathematical formulae. While this is a disadvantage it is not fatal, but the figures showing growth or change must be studied. For instance, if one is studying Australia or New Zealand one should be fully aware of how recent growth are the present numbers. The present population of New Zealand is 1,642,000 (1939), but it only reached 1,000,000 in 1911 and in 1851 it was 27,000. Such a population has been and still is essentially a pioneering one, though it is now passing out of that stage. The Australian population dates from 1788 but was only 190,000 in 1840, just over a century ago. It jumped up in the next decade to 405,000 chiefly because of the gold rush. It was 1,145,000 in 1860. It did not reach the figure of 5,000,000 till the Great War. The U.S.A. figures are even more spectacular.

All the European populations, including Great Britain, also show very remarkable growth, a fact often forgotten by historians. Thus one factor in French domination of the continent in the early 18th century was the relatively large population of France compared with her neighbours.

This great growth in numbers in the 19th century can be attributed (1) to the constantly increasing knowledge in medicine and hygiene; (2) to improved techniques in production; (3) to the development of the Americas and Australasia in particular. It affected primarily the white peoples so that we see the appearance of dense populations in Europe and the development of white populations elsewhere. We thus have the spectacle of the expanding and prosperous 19th century. This rapid rise in numbers accompanied by an equally rapid rise in the standards of living among the west European peoples and those overseas is one which demands the geographer's attention. It should be contrasted with the problems confronting India and China. Can they too achieve the same result? Are the conditions the same? In such a discussion the achievements of Japan and Soviet Russia must needs be considered. There is not time or space here for discussion but it is the type of problem which should challenge and interest us.

After considering the actual numbers and their growth one

must turn to the sex proportions and to the size of the various age groups as these affect the amount of labour available for production. How they do so and to what extent depends partly upon purely physical facts and partly upon custom. Thus women's labour from the physical aspect must in general be confined to the less heavy tasks. It is interesting to note how soon women gave up certain kinds of war work and handed it back to the men. Just as it is interesting to note how in those countries where women are forced to continue in heavy work they age quickly and die earlier. Custom, however, is vastly important. Sometimes it is the outcome of long racial experience, sometimes mere prejudice, and always it tends to be connected directly or indirectly with the fact that women are the mothers and so must look after the homes and the children. How much of this is instinctive is open to considerable discussion. So with children. The tendency in modern countries is to raise the school-leaving age. In our own it is now 15 for all. It will be remembered how much the discussion of the Ten Hours Bill of 1847 turned upon the interdependence of the men upon women's and children's help. What is the ratio of males to females depends upon many factors. It should be noted, however, that there are always more males born than females, but the male is a delicate creature and dies more easily. In India there is a proverb which runs to the effect that one cannot take too much care of a boy-baby but that the girl-babies can be put on the door mat and will look after themselves. Maybe some of my readers will think this is a somewhat biased statement. But statistics show that as the age advances so do the females predominate. After early childhood it is due to industrial and other accidents which take a steady toll of men: partly, in certain countries such as our own, it is due to migration which always shows a heavy excess of males: partly during the past generation it is due to the great slaughters of the two wars. Countries such as Canada, New Zealand or any country with a stream of immigrants generally show an excess of males just as they show greater percentages of adults of working age.

The size of the age groups depends upon the birth and death rates. Thus in a country with a rapidly growing population there will be a high proportion of children and a relatively low one of elderly and aged. The opposite will be true where a population is declining. The certainty that the elderly and old age groups in this country will be very high in the next two decades raises a problem which will present itself for solution in due course.

The size of the age groups and the sex ratio affect production in two ways. In the first way by offering or withholding certain kinds of labour, and in the second through their influence on demand. Children need many things not required by adults: old people again have their particular demands.

So far we have neglected two very important factors from the geographical point of view, namely, density and distribution of a population. These must always be considered with reference to physical conditions, the techniques of production and standards of living. Mere references to mean average densities are worse than useless. In fact the beginner in geography is well-advised to keep away from the use of averages or mean averages. Such figures, unless accompanied by a mass of detailed knowledge, are a snare. It is like the mean annual rainfall of Karachi which is about 3 inches, but that is not Nature's way. Nothing happens for two or three years and then it all falls at once with the resulting deluge and floods. So with mean annual temperatures. Apparently two kinds of hell when averaged can make a paradise. Averages are only safe when employed by the initiated. Thus, take the case of India which is generally thought and rightly so to be an over-populated country. This could be proved to the contrary by figures of average density, for India as a unit has only 195 per square mile which is much the same as Europe without Russia. What was British India has about 235 while the Indian States are about 110. The former exceeds the ratio density for France by a little while the latter is practically the same as that of Spain. Local variations are, however, very great as may be seen from the following selected figures. Baluchistan, which is slightly larger than the British Isles, has an average population of only 6·5 to the square mile. The reasons are soon obvious when one knows the country. Actually most of the population is very densely packed in a few narrow valleys where water makes cultivation possible.

Bengal presents a very different picture with an average of about 779 (1941) which is many more than in any country in Europe except Great Britain and Belgium. Its density is far greater than that of any other Indian province. Most of Bengal is a fertile alluvial or diluvial plain in which rice is the predominant crop. The Sunderbans proper are practically uninhabited and the hill region to the north only sparsely: so also is the western border near Chotia Nagpur except Ranigang. Elsewhere population is fairly evenly distributed:

Burdwan Division	728
Presidency ,,	781
Rajshahi ,,	613
Dacca ,,	1,077
Chittagong ,,	721

The Punjab has an average of 287 but the districts vary considerably:

Himalayan	78
Sub-Himalayan	305
North West Area	99
Indo Gangetic Plain W.	286

These figures are, however, very misleading as they are themselves averages. If one takes the population per cultivated square mile they are 965, 612, 482, and 435 respectively.

The same kinds of differences show themselves in China, but one cannot get such precise statistical data. Some approximate figures are available in the Statistical Summary in Cressey's *China's Geographical Foundations*.

To turn to our own country one notes that the great bulk of the population is in England with only 1/5 in Scotland, Ireland and Wales.

A careful study of a few such examples will show that it is impossible to say whether a country is full or empty without laying down a great number of qualifying conditions. That is why much that is written about 'optimum populations' can be so unconvincing. In such discussion we must state explicitly what are our premises. The conclusions arrived at will be valid with reference only to these premises. Thus the optimum population for a holiday resort may be one thing for a coster-monger from the East End of London and another for a bird-watcher.

The degree of urbanisation must be noted. This is partly a matter of definition. Unless the official definitions are known any comparison of urban and rural populations can be very misleading. Here are a few definitions:

Australia: Year Book 1944-5: page 463, para. 5. This does not tell us anything definite and one would need to make further inquiries. It would be helpful to the general inquirer if the authorities could be more explicit.

New Zealand: The Year Book for 1937, page 846, includes in urban population any number exceeding 1,000, which makes about 60·7% urban. This can be misleading to those who think of urban in terms of the United Kindgom.

India: The Census for 1931 (vol. I, part 1, para. 37) has an elaborate note which is worth reading. The minimum figure for urban is 5,000 but this was not always observed for various reasons. In the Census for 1941 (page 46, para. 1) a protest was made by the Registrar about this tendency to lower the figure and the reader is warned that 5,000 will be adhered to.

Canada: Year Book 1947, p. 101. No definite figure is laid down. "The distinction between rural and urban populations in Canada, therefore, is a distinction of provincial legal status rather than of size. Since the laws of the various provinces differ . . . the line of demarcation between rural and urban population is not uniformly drawn throughout the Dominion."

For the U.S.A. (Stat. Abs. 1946, p. 2) the figure is 2,500. The Americans further divide their rural population into farm and non-farm—a useful division.

Where there is a high urbanisation, whether due to mining or manufacture, there must be a counterbalancing rural population as towns must be supplied both with foodstuffs and raw mater-ials. This is often forgotten both by geographers and the man in the street who seem to take it for granted, or did, that loaves and fishes appear of themselves in the towns. It explains the facile suggestion that the solution for the hungry millions in India is industrialisation and urbanisation. Without a radical change in the countryside the millions would still be hungry and unemployed. We too in this country have begun to learn this bitter truth.

Finally, it is not sufficient to count heads. The quality of the population is even more important than its numbers. This quality is affected by physical, mental and moral considerations.

On the physical side the make-up of the higher age groups is important. The increase on the length of life is of little advantage to a country economically. From this point of view it would be better if elderly folk die at, say, 65. The proportion of old people is going up very greatly of late but old people do not produce much. Then the general physical condition matters much, a discovery which was made long ago as regards animals but which has only begun to be realised during the last generation when two great wars have emphasised physical fitness. There is no doubt that some progress has been made in this direction in Great Britain though the superior physique of the men from the Dominions and the U.S. point to the need for more effort.

Mental conditions matter more as time goes on. There is no room for uneducated workers of whatever grade. Education is generally thought of in terms of technical education of which there can never be enough, but technical education is the least important. General and cultural education are fundamental and without these the technicians will not take us far. The writer when talking once to a Bagdadi Jew who was a great cloth merchant mentioned the decline of Lancashire, and in the discussion which followed the merchant attributed much of the Lancashire decline to lack of general education. This statement must not be pressed too far but it contains an important truth. Sir Hugh Bell somewhere records a conversation with a German ironmaster who said, "We Germans, when we began, had to change our professors into business men: you English have never changed your business men into professors." One

of the disastrous effects of the present policy of 'utility' is that
the young generation are being deprived of an essential part of
their cultural education which must show itself in the quality
of the worker later.   For those who cannot appreciate good
quality in living become incapable of it in their work.

Lastly, there is the question of morale.   Neither good physique nor education avail without a good morale.   Morale is a
question of morals in the narrower and broader sense.   Too
little attention has been paid to this in civil life.   It is lack of
morale which is holding us back in this country today.

So far we have been considering the economics of population;
now let us see how this can be applied geographically.   One
might first look at the world's total population and see how it is
distributed.   For this the best source is the Statistical Year
Book of the League of Nations.   The figure given there for
1939 is 2,170,000,000 on a superficial land area of 53,200,000
square miles.   All these figures must be used with care but for
general rough purposes we will accept them.   A second easily
available source is *Whitakers' Almanac*.   The chapter entitled
"the World" gives all the figures.   They don't correspond
accurately with the League of Nations Year Book but the
approximation is sufficiently close for our purpose which is
merely a rough estimate.   Let us take the table in Whitaker.

	sq. miles	population
Europe	2,085,000	397,000,000
Asia	10,348,000	1,124,000,000
U.S.S.R.	8,176,000	170,000,000
Africa	11,699,000	154,000,000
N. America	7,581,000	141,000,000
C. America and Islands	1,077,000	40,000,000
S. America	7,047,000	90,000,000
Oceania	3,201,000	11,000,000
Total	51,214,000	2,127,000,000
L. of N. totals	53,200,000	2,170,000,000

It doesn't tell us much and what it does say may easily be mis-represented. We can note superficially that Europe is relatively more densely populated than Asia. On the other hand Africa is comparatively empty and Oceania which is mainly Aus-tralia has very few people. But we are not interested here in the superficial area. One might note that in their propaganda for *lebensraum* the Germans deliberately used this crude method of taking total area for misleading opinion. It is the available area that counts. First let us consider the cultivable land for this will determine the optimum size of the world's population and will be an important factor in determining the present dis-tribution of world population. There are others which can be considered later. How do we estimate the amount of cultivable land? That must of necessity be an arbitrary definition. Land producing say 30 bushels of wheat to the acre is obviously cultivable. Much land only produces 10 bushels. Some would produce only five and, no doubt, some one. Anything that can be cultivated is cultivable. The limiting factor is the cost per unit of production. It is this which makes the use of agricul-tural statistics so difficult and dangerous. No two countries have the same definitions. But to come back to our question of how much of the earth's surface is cultivable. There is a good discussion on this in 'The Food Supply in the Migration Process' by Carl L. Alsberg in Bowman's *Limits of Land Settlement*. Here the cultivated area is whittled down to something between 5·5 to 6 million square miles. This might be added to making a total of, say, 10 million square miles. That makes 6,400 million acres for something over 2,000 million people, a matter of 3·2 acres per head. "In addition, each could have more or less agriculturally productive-land not arable, to use for grazing or for tree crops. We cannot say how much but probably about as much as he could have arable. This amount—let us say, 6 acres all told—would be sufficient . . . at present the world gets along without using as much as 2 acres of arable land per head of population" (p. 43).

Here then is a rough figure to work on—it is no more. Let us accept it for the sake of argument. We are trying to estimate the optimum population for the world—an extremely dangerous

thing to do in the writer's opinion. For that we should have
to decide how much and what kind of food the average person
consumes. Are we to take the U.S. standard, our own as laid
down by an all-wise government or the Indian? Let us take
our own as it was pre-war. If all the world were to be fed at
that level, then the present 3·2 acres would not suffice. The
greater part of the Asiatic peoples are underfed and badly fed
by our standards. Whitaker's has a charming little footnote
on page 236 which reads, "It has been estimated that the Earth
can maintain a population of 6,000,000,000 a total which will
be reached about A.D. 2100 at the present rate of increase."
I doubt it, for from this cultivable area must come all the commercial crops such as cotton, etc. We should need to know a
good deal about the techniques and standards of production.
No doubt these can be greatly, even vastly, improved in most
countries of the world but agricultural change is slow especially
in the peasant countries. Further, one can take it that in general
the best lands are already under cultivation. This is so in
Europe, North America, Asia and Africa. The remaining three
million square miles are not so good as those now cultivated.
It does not mean that much good land or potentially good land
does not remain. There are vast stretches in South America,
much in North America, some in Asia, but they will require
great capital investment in the way of irrigation, drainage,
transport development, clearance. Thus no doubt most of the
Amazon basin is a potential agricultural area and might be
turned into a gigantic Java. But what capital, labour and
science would be necessary! True, if this mad world had devoted to the conquest of the Amazon basin all that was devoted to
destruction these past years, much might have been done.
But then they did not and will not. Man's superhuman efforts
up to date are nearly always devoted to destruction, not construction. It would be as well, therefore, if the world's population did not grow.

   The inequalities in numbers as between countries are largely
though not wholly explained when one begins to examine the
physical and climatic conditions. The great stretches of cold
and hot desert explain themselves: the semi-arid areas though

capable of development can never maintain more than a slight population. Do not overestimate the possibilities of dry-farming which must mean large capital expenditure and small outputs per acre. Large outputs per capita are only possible with very large mechanised farms. All such lands will be sparsely populated. It might be argued in that case that North America should have a much higher population than it does: so also South America. So probably they would, had they been open to certain Asiatic peoples or even the European, five hundred years ago. Why the Red Indians did not breed and develop an agriculture similar to that in India or China must be left to the anthropologist: the white races came relatively late, and owing to their insistence upon high levels of consumption and the practice of family limitation of late years numbers have kept lower than they might otherwise have been. In the past a limiting factor to the levelling up in population densities was the difficulty of moving. It is only in the last hundred years that the great movements have been made possible. Today a limiting factor is the immigration laws of those countries which have empty or relatively empty lands. Australia needs immigrants to develop her resources but refuses Asiatics. So too the North American peoples.

While one is dealing with migration perhaps a digression might be allowed here as emigration and immigration, while they have played very important roles especially in the 19th and 20th centuries, can be overestimated in their effects. Emigration is advocated on the grounds that it relieves population pressure. It all depends. One case only stands out where population fell as a result of emigration, i.e. Ireland, where numbers fell from over 8,000,000 to about 4,500,000. There was an outstanding example of an excessive population finding relief. In the case of England and Scotland population still continued to grow as the emigration was less than the natural increase. How much the pressure was relieved is hard to measure. In many cases the relief is nil. If one takes the case of Italy which sent out great numbers of emigrants during the 19th and early 20th centuries one is inclined to believe that it was only to the cemeteries that relief came. As the emigrants went population pressure tended to fall, so that living conditions were made a little less intolerable for those at the lower end. The death rates fell somewhat. Let us look at India and China with their surplus populations. Both have a relatively high birth rate, that of India being 33 per thousand: both have high death rates yet the Indian population increased by 51,000,000 in the decade 1931–41. Given what would be called a reasonable death rate in Western Europe, the rate of growth could easily be about 8,000,000 a year. Emigration to reduce the population would, therefore, have to be over 8,000,000 a year. It is when one contemplates these vast populations that emigration is shown to be of practically no help. This raises a problem to which we will refer later.

Let us now take a few examples. There is a great belt of dense population which occupies a large part of England, Belgium, Germany, Silesia and even stretches, though the density is less, into the Donetz basin. Correlate this with the coal-fields and the coincidence is marked. Here is a highly organised and industrialised population based upon coal extraction and the heavy industries. Coal and iron have accounted largely for these agglomerations. Coal being power partly accounts for Lancashire. Once the peoples were there with all their internal and external economics, to use the economist's phrase, that is, with all their outfits for working and living, they tended to attract the newer industries. This great belt is essentially an urbanised one: the regions do not feed themselves but depend upon the sale of their manufactures to pay for their food-stuffs and raw materials. They are excess importers of these things. Such agglomerations are only possible with modern transport and can only properly exist in a world which permits of easy trading. Note that the density is made up of high concentrations. The countryside may be relatively sparsely peopled in contrast to, say, the Nile delta, the Red Basin of China, the Pearl River delta, the North China Plain, or Bengal. Here too are regions of dense population but this time they are rural. The great industrial towns are lacking. In place of high urban concentrations we find a heavily spread rural population which is practically self-supporting but which lives at a low standard,

Modern industry has not yet touched them though the population problem of some is being aggravated as modern medicine lowers the death rates.

On the other hand many regions even in Asia surprise one by their low population density. Such a one is Assam, Burma is another, Sumatra another. Contrast Sumatra with the adjacent Java, one teeming with a dense agricultural population, the other until very recently almost empty. It is easy to account for the emptiness of the Arabian desert or the Sahara but the other cases will not be explained geographically. There are historical and human reasons, also one must allow for accident and chance. There are times in the writer's opinion when we can be too logical in historical and human affairs. A concatenation of events is only inevitable after they are over, not before. There is always a chance. What would have happened in Europe if Lieutenant Buonaparte had been shot dead in his first action or if Corporal Adolf Hitler also had been killed? There are, however, those who are scientific fatalists and who will not agree with me.

So empty regions, full regions, half-full regions should be a challenge to the geographer. One thing they should never be, just a dull fact. For we geographers are not merely after facts but the 'why' behind them.

Finally it should be remembered of what very recent growth the present dense populations are and how recent the techniques by which they are maintained and which we take for granted today. Let us go back 70 years, not a very long time, taking a few countries at random.

	1870	1939
U.S.A.	38,500,000	131,000,000
Canada	3,700,000	11,370,000
Japan	34,300,000	72,520,000
India	206,000,000	389,000,000
Germany	41,100,000	69,000,000
Egypt	5,000,000	16,650,000
N. Zealand	255,000	1,642,000
Italy	26,800,000	44,000,000

	1870	1939
Russia	76,500,000	146,000,000
France	36,100,000	41,200,000
England & Wales	22,700,000	41,660,000

The growth of the European peoples is the outstanding fact of the 19th century. Today is witnessing the growth of the Asiatic peoples once more with the resultant pressures. These world population pressures are important. So far they have taken place almost unnoticed. It is like steam pressure in a boiler: it can go on rising until the maximum pressure for which the boiler has been built is reached. After that anything may happen. The present techniques of production are very new and are more and more based upon scientific research, but it does not alter the fact that in a developing world on the western scale pressure of demand for raw materials will tend to outstrip supply. This again raises problems of world distribution. But there we must leave it for the moment.

CHAPTER IV

TYPES OF CULTURE AND STANDARDS OF LIVING

THE things which people want and consume are a reflexion of their tastes, their customs and their cultures. As we economic geographers are concerned with the production and consumption of goods it is very necessary to consider the various cultural developments and the different standards of living of the many and various communities which together make up the economic world. The type of culture will affect incentives and methods of production and thus the standards of living and these, in their turn, will react upon cultural development. Again it is the organic relationship. It is quite impossible to neglect this non-economic aspect of community life. The writer believes that the non-economic factors are more important than the economic, or at least as important, in the life of a people and does not subscribe to the doctrine of the economic interpretation of history. The body and its demands are important but the spirit is more so. It is this interaction which makes the art of medicine so difficult. People are cured by more than drugs: black magic does work in Africa and cheerfulness is a great cure for dyspepsia.

This brings us to the study of anthropology which is far from being an academic matter. The economic geographer ought to know something of the principal civilisations of the world, such as those of China, India and Islam. He must know something of the primitive peoples of Africa, Polynesia and elsewhere, but that is not enough. He must come close home and study the European peoples including the British. Anthropologists have tended until recently to confine their studies to the primitive peoples or to the civilisations distinct from our own. This is very natural but it can be misleading. The Pacific taboos can fill one with astonishment and even amusement, for we British are prone to be amused at customs strange to us, but a little thought will show that taboos are equally common with us. That is one of the advantages of anthropological study, it helps us to see ourselves. It is very necessary when we are remodelling the world in a hurry to know not only something of human nature as such, though that is pretty much the same whatever our colour or cranial index, but also about human nature as it has been conditioned by a thousand years of careful schooling. A Chinese baby born in England and brought up entirely by English people would become a little Englishman, that is, if the real British babies, children and adults would forget his yellow face and slit eyes and not rub it in that he wasn't. An English baby taken to the U.S. grows up an American, but when 300,000,000 people have been living together in relative isolation as did the Chinese till recently they get a point of view of their own and certain common resemblances. When the Polish Division came to Cambridge during the war the men all looked as if they had had the same parents, and what was even more important the insides of their heads were as different from ours as the outsides. Values are different, tastes vary, likes and dislikes obtrude.

One would suggest then a little reading: Page's *Primitive Races of Today* which is a readable and pleasant introduction. As an alternative though probably more difficult to procure there is *Our Primitive Contemporaries* by G. P. Murdock. This fills in a good many gaps in Page and is a larger book. It is published in New York. A small book called *Human Types* by R. Frith is useful to look at. It belongs to the "Discussion Series". Two books of outstanding interest and vigour are *At Home with the Savage* and *The Savage as he Really is*, by J. H. Driberg. Driberg wrote from first hand knowledge. He really loved the savage, and never made that fatal mistake so common to us civilised beings of treating him as a museum piece or as rather a quaint grown-up child. When you can really talk to these people you find they are very human and to them the life they lead is the normal and commonplace. What a pity savages can't write books about us. On caste, O'Malley's *Caste in India* is a simple introduction. Hutton's book is much fuller and more erudite. I doubt if the beginner will get much out of it until he has read something simpler. Caste, however, is not simple and any attempt to make it so must mislead. The only excuse for simplifying is that which one has when teaching history to children. One can hardly put a ten volume history into the hands of a child of ten. The little books must be distorted through compression. One teaches in this way hoping to expand and correct the falsification gradually. W. Crooke's *Natives of Northern India* is very readable, but I doubt if it is easily available outside fairly big libraries. For Asia in general *The Peoples of Asia* by L. D. Dudley-Buxton is very readable. For Europe one might try Huxley and Haddon, *We Europeans*. This must have been a most unpopular piece of work in Nazi Germany. When you have read it you will know what mongrels we Europeans are. It is not too easy to read but a very necessary book to right and sound thinking. One will be careful afterwards when talking about 'races' of pure blood. Haddon's *Races of Man* is exceedingly compressed and one hesitates to recommend it to a beginner. Two small introductory books can be found in the Home University Library, *Anthropology* by R. R. Marret and the *Dawn of History* by J. R. Myers, both very good. While reading about savages and the Asiatic civilisations one should remember to watch closely the modern European. Ask yourself in what way an Englishman differs from a Welshman, a Scot and an Irishman, and why he manages to rub them up the wrong way so often. All the time one should be doing 'field work' as far as it is possible. There have been ample opportunities of studying the European peoples and Americans of late without even leaving one's village or street.

Let us consider a few cases to show how culture can affect economic life and so be of interest to us as economic geographers. Religious ideals can greatly affect economic activity. The Hindu religion is essentially a religion of negation as regards this life rather in the way that the ultra Puritan attitude can be only more so. Life for the Hindu is illusion, a dream, and mostly it is a bad dream. The great desire is to fall into a sound slumber, but this is not easy. One falls out of one dream into another. This is the doctrine of reincarnation and of

Karma. How can one attain this dreamless sleep or nirvana? Only by denying the human desires and passions. Hence the emphasis on passivity. To the Buddhist also—who is not a Hindu—all action is to be avoided whether good or bad as it leads to reincarnation. Hence all action is to be depreciated. Given such religious and philosophical backgrounds one would not find many hundred per cent go-getters. True not all Hindus practice their religion any more than do the so-called Christians, but it is an attitude which retards effort. Contrast this with the Protestant attitude that sloth is ungodly: that work can be a form of prayer and that this world is far from being a delusion and the results will be obvious. Not that all Englishmen are such good Protestants. Mingled with it in our case is the cricket culture with its three-day match which reveals a philosophy which is also unlikely to produce go-getters. And who shall say that either Hindu or Englishman are wholly wrong? Now let us look very briefly at the caste system. Here is something peculiar to India just as the monsoon may be said to be the outstanding fact in India's rainfall. Class distinctions in varying degrees of rigidity and intensity can be found in many parts of the world, but nowhere is there anything like the rigidity and minute division which is found in India. This not only affects eating and inter-marrying, which are indeed the main concern of caste, but it stops men working. Certain kinds of work are unclean or outside of the caste permissions and so cannot be done except by low caste men or outcastes. For a higher caste man to do such work would mean social ruin. It certainly affects the mobility of labour not only from place to place but from one type of work to another. It is interesting to note that just when the rigidities of caste are being softened so that labour is made more mobile in India the Trade Unions of this country are working in the opposite direction. There are in India something like 50,000,000 outcastes or as they are now called scheduled castes. These people are social pariahs. The treatment they have received during the past 1,000 years makes their uplift no easy problem. One great effect of caste among many was to make the upper or literate castes unpractical, so that modern India has had to wait until very recent times for leaders capable of understanding present day industry and its problems.

Then when studying agriculture in India we meet the Hindu attitude to cattle. The cow is sacred. To kill a cow for a good and orthodox Hindu is the equivalent to murder with us. The Hindu is genuinely shocked and revolted at the thought of eating beef which to him is like cannabilism to us. The whole attitude seems to us absurd. Surely one only needs a little common sense and everything could be put right. So the Mohammedan might argue with the equally foolish English-woman or man who is shocked at the idea of polygamy. One has to realise that these beliefs are passionately held. It took the writer some time before he fully realised this fact. Again, take the Mohammedan with his instinctive horror of the pig. We can have trouble even with modern Indian students on these matters of beef or bacon. Yet modern farming demands that the farmer shall take a rational view of his animals. They are there for use and nothing else; to be cared for while useful but to be destroyed as soon as they are not. The Hindu will not kill off his diseased or old cattle. They wander about eating fodder which should go to the healthy animals. Fodder is always scarce in India. Yet dairy farming on a modern pattern can never begin until these diseased and worse than useless animals are destroyed. Probably 45% of all Indian cattle could be destroyed to the advantage of the country. Many of my readers will have seen these miserable animals when in India. It has been proved on the Government experimental stations and farms that magnificent animals both for milk and traction can be bred out of these beasts. So it is with the pig. The Indian pig is a horror as it roots and grubs among the village garbage, so also is the Indian dog, both animals taking the place of drain pipes and incinerators. The religious ban on the pig in the East is really a sanitary ban as the Eastern pig is so full of parasites and disease that he would be a very unwise person who ate the flesh of so foul a creature. The ban, however, prevents the intro-duction of the European pig and so deprives the farmer of a profit-making animal and the country of a source of meat supply. It will take long to make the change. However one must be careful in one's generalisation, the non-Hindu of whom the Moslems are the largest group, will eat beef with pleasure and other forms of meat too, such as mutton and goat, but these must be killed the proper way, that is the same way as is demanded by the Jews. Moslems will not eat beef killed our way with the blood left in the animal. This being so it would not be of much use for the Chicago meat packers to start an 'eat more beef' campaign in India. Modern mixed farming would be possible with Moslems and thus a beef industry would be possible in Pakistan. How long will it take to bring about a radical change among these teeming millions?

The cult of the cow is not confined to India. One finds a similar attitude though less deeply rooted among many of the African peoples. The Bantu woman will not feel herself properly married unless cattle have been paid. It is not a case of 'buying' a wife as some misguided people think. To the woman it is necessary for decency and respectability. As well ask an English bride to marry without a wedding-ring or a marriage certificate. Few are so advanced that they do not demand these. The dethronement of cattle to these people, therefore, upsets their social system. Yet it means that the Reserves are gravely overstocked by almost useless beasts. So it is in Kenya among the Masai and in Uganda. There is however one difference compared with India. These people in general will eat beef. In the old days before white control, when raiding was a normal way of passing the time and keeping both human and animal populations in control, the raiders had no qualms in eating their neighbours' cattle. It was only their own they hesitated over and even these they ate sometimes. It is easier to begin the change and already in Uganda much progress has been made in this direction.

The geographer must take account of religion wherever he finds it, for especially with the more primitive peoples and those still unaffected by modern scientific thought, religion and superstition form a very real part of the environment in which men think and act. So it did in medieval Europe and with us until the last century. It is the fashion to scoff at this, pointing out the inhumanities of the Victorian period, but it should be asked what might have happened if that slight tincture of religion had gone. The answer can be found in the concentration camps and other horrors of Nazi Germany or in the Japanese cruelties. Indeed the fanaticism of the Nazi and the communist is a substitute for religion as men cannot exist without one. Read Huxley's *Brave New World*.

Attitudes to food also matter greatly. The rice eaters of China, Japan or India eat rice by preference not merely of necessity. This comes out in such novels as *The Good Earth* and *Rice*. During the late famine in Bengal part of the trouble lay in the fact that the people would only eat millets or wheat when almost starved. They wanted rice. In Japan the 'better' people eat certain types of Japanese grown rice which is preferred because of its superior taste. Those going up the social scale aspire also to this distinction. It is bad form to eat imported rice as it was among some in this country to eat imported meat or to drink Indian tea. Not all these preferences are mere snobbery. It is possible to have a cultivated taste. French people with more educated palates than ours dislike English food and most people prefer the French wines. This last preference is of vast importance to the French viticulturalists and to their export trade.

Coming nearer home we shall still find contrasts though less strongly marked, at least to us. If one travelled in that Europe which is now almost wholly destroyed one would have noticed the cultural differences from one country to another, each and all in their several ways affecting production. The glassblowers and workers of Venice and in Italy, where can one find their equals? The artistry of the French and the Italians have behind them a long history stretching back through the centuries during which their cultures were evolved. Should the reader ever go to Harvard University let him look at the glass flowers, the exquisite product of a rare combination of German and Italian. What other combination of culture and technique could have produced them? Perhaps the Chinese or the Japanese might have done so. One notes the disciplined patience and laboriousness of the German, the product of a long evolution which made the German people as formidable in industry and commerce as it did in war,

c*

and contrast it with French lightness and imagination which have made them the centre of the Western world for women's fashions and for that infinite variety of things which make up the 'luxury' exports of France. So, too, it is with the better French fabrics, especially silk. In all these ways culture affects production and commerce.

Cultures have negative effects as well as positive. The unique culture of Tibet has resulted in the complete isolation and economic stagnation of that country. Given the physical setting life could never be easy in Tibet nor could communication be anything but costly as well as difficult. Nevertheless here is a theocratic state which has subordinated all else to the religious life. Whether that religion and its products are good or bad is not our affair here but it is quite obvious that any study of Tibet even commercially must begin and end with its religious beliefs and practices.

So far we have dealt with culture as it affects man's economic activities but have thought of it as a common culture diffused over a considerable region. It is possible to speak of an Indian culture in spite of the fact that Madrasis differ very greatly from Bengalis and both from Punjabis. So too one can talk of a European culture. In both cases the differences are those of tones and shades but we cannot omit those regions where the clash of cultures is obvious and prominent, for these clashes cause grave social strains and stresses which have serious repercussions upon economic activities. Such clashes are most easily seen in the differences of colour whether it be white and black or what you will. South Africa stands out as the strongest example but is far from being the only one. Here white and black meet but refuse to mix in the true sense. Let it be said at once that the writer is not sitting in judgment upon the South Africans, but as a geographer he must watch the economic effect of this clash just as a psychoanalyst watches the mental clashes which make for nervous breakdowns. A wise missionary once remarked when talking of colour that it was not fundamentally a clash of colour so much as a clash of cultures, but generally the sharp dividing lines of culture coincided with those of colour. That is true. One cannot live intimately with those of a completely different culture, and history shows that many of the great struggles are culture struggles. The statement, however, is not complete for the cultural antagonism is identified with colour even when through common education it has itself disappeared. Thus an African, however cultured and educated from our point of view, will find it difficult to get into the average home in this country. No 'coloured' person finds life easy here no matter how well educated he or she may be.

In South Africa the whites and the Bantu blacks both entered the country about the same time, the one from the south-west and the other from the north-east: neither are native to the country. The natives were Bushmen who were chivvied away by the Hottentots and kindred tribes until all were squeezed between the whites and the Bantu. It is well to remember this as it disposes of the question of proprietary rights. Given the times, and the method of meeting, frontier clashes, the ferocity on both sides developed soon into a colour feeling of great intensity. In South Africa the dominating emotion of the whites is fear. Not only are they a small minority 2 : 9 but behind the black population stands the whole of Africa, and Africa has been watching Asia and dreaming dreams. Whatever might have been had all the whites from the first behaved as good Christians is of little import. What we as geographers have to do is to look at things as they now are: a white minority physically afraid, but even more afraid of losing jobs should the native become educated. The white of whatever class has a strong vested interest. This combines with other emotions to make a rigid barrier socially and economically, for even economically the black man is only admitted for purely utilitarian purposes. The South African, like the white man everywhere, would like to get rid of the African if that were possible, which it is not as he is useful in the mines, in domestic work, on the farms. When not wanted he goes back to his Reserves. The system of Reserves is an attempt to have one's cake and eat it. To change the metaphor it is like the brass bottle of the Arabian Nights; the stopper is taken out and the Afrite appears, does what he is commanded and goes back into his bottle till next wanted. If the native population were static the Reserves might serve this purpose, but population grows and the pressures within the Reserves grow also.

The thinking South Africans are perturbed for the future as is witnessed in their Commission reports, and there is a growing feeling among the better informed that educational and social uplift are necessary if a healthy solution is to be found.   At present the colour bar prevents the native learning skilled trades. Within the Reserves the native has been left to his own devices until the overstocking of the land is leading to very serious land erosion.   All this can be found in the "Drought Report" which unfortunately is out of print.   At the moment then the South Africans are in a dilemma.   Population is growing, both white and black: the easily available resources of the past are no longer so plentiful, while certain evils such as soil erosion and under-nourishment among the black population are increasing.   The old outlets of employment for the whites, agriculture and mining, are not sufficient to absorb the increasing numbers and so new ones must be found.   This is being done by developing industry and by the 'civilised labour' policy.   The problem of the black man remains and grows.   He is a slovenly agriculturalist: an inefficient farm labourer and without skill for trades.   All this for two reasons: no serious attempt has been made to educate him in either the narrow or broad sense and he is debarred from acquiring most of the skills for fear he should compete with the white workman.   In general education and culture almost nothing has been done, so that while he has been detribalised and has lost his tribal virtues and culture he is unable to understand and appreciate those of the white.   We cannot educate men in negatives.   Apart from some missionary work and a very little Government effort, very little, the South Africa Bantu has had no positive education.   It is a case of the man out of whom the unclean spirit was cast.   It takes very considerable time, several generations, to turn a savage into a modern work-man and citizen.   It is not only a difficult but a painful process as he suffers from spiritual and mental indigestion.   What we have achieved in this country after half a millennium of slow change he is supposed to do in a lifetime, and cannot.   Such a change would require of the teacher infinite patience and understanding as well as active goodwill, for the black man is no angel. The faults and failings of the South African black can easily be accounted for but not so easily eliminated. The stark fact, however, stands out that here is an economy trying to work in two overlapping but antagonistic worlds. Nevertheless the black man has had his revenge as do all servile peoples upon their masters for he has compelled his white master to accept many of his standards. If the farmer cannot raise the standard of his labour he must accept theirs. Moreover it makes a dilemma. Not all white men are competent and able. Some can only do unskilled work and even then with qualifications. These low grade whites must compete with the black and cannot: just as the urbanised black cannot compete with the one just come from the Reserves. Each forces the other down, and so is created not only the 'poor white' problem but also a poor detribalised black one as well. South Africa is turning to manufacture, but finds that the South African white is the highest paid workman in the world though his relative efficiency does not correspond to his wages. So far he has solved the problem by depressing the black man's wages. This means that the millions of blacks make a negligible market for manufactured goods as they have little purchasing power. The South African products are not cheap because of the high wages of the whites and export is unlikely so that the home market must absorb the products. This confines the buyers very largely to the whites and so means a constricted market. Meantime the mass of the population, which is black, is condemned to poverty.

The problem has been stated very crudely and briefly for lack of space but it illustrates the contention that cultures and their effects cannot be neglected. The problem presents itself in the Southern States of the U.S., though with local modifications. Here it is less intense as the white majority is marked. Also the negro is much more sophisticated. The white Australia policy is based upon a realisation of these cultural differences and difficulties. Here one might note that the white Australia policy is directed more at Asiatics such as the Japanese, Chinese and Indians. A similar attitude is maintained in Canada and California. In these cases the feeling of racial superiority is not the dominant factor, for whatever reason there might be for such an attitude towards the African, there can be none such towards the Asiatic with his own high types of civilisation and cultural attainments. No doubt it is there but the dominant motive is economic fear that these people by their skill, their thriftiness and patient labour will drive out the American or European who would not be able to compete. There is also the fear that their rapid growth of numbers will sooner or later submerge the indigenous white population. There is no doubt that an Australia or New Zealand open to unrestricted Asiatic immigration would soon cease to be white. Penrose in his *Population Theories* denies this, maintaining that the immigrants would adopt the higher standards of living of their new country and so the birth rate would fall. It depends of course upon the rate of inflow. For a trickle we would agree, but not for a heavy sustained flow. Here some, certainly the Asiatic, might reply. Why not? There is no answer to such a question. The white Australia policy is based upon emotion rationalised as are all such policies: upon a preference for one's own race and one's own type of culture and living. It is equally marked among the Asiatic peoples.

Let us now turn to another aspect of this cultural cleavage, that of human migration. Given the world's unequal distribution of natural wealth there are two major ways in which it can be adjusted to population, one is migration and the other trade. These are two sides of the same coin. Either goods can be taken to the people or the people can be taken to the goods. Migration is only possible as a continuous process (1) if the migrating peoples are permitted to enter or, failing that, can force their way into the regions where they desire to settle, and (2) when the immigrants can be absorbed into the receiving society so that they lose their original identity and become merged culturally and spiritually in their new home. When the two peoples thus brought together are unable to amalgamate for whatsoever reason, there must be friction which may be slight as between French and English Canadian or extreme as in Palestine today. Where there can be no compatibility the tendency today is to limit or prevent immigration.

The economic consequences of such policies can be very great.

So far one has considered cultures as causes of conflict and friction which either retard or prevent production and these are the most important aspects, but there is a further one which is of lesser importance though still important. Goods as we have seen can be divided into consumption and capital goods, i.e. those which are produced for use in living and those which are made for further production. Examples of these types are clothes and say looms. Cultures show their preferences more in consumer goods and it is interesting to watch all these little differences which affect trade, though it is more interesting to watch the differences for their own sake. It raises a point which may be a side issue but which may be more. The modern planned world based upon pseudo-science aims at the regimentation of life. Everyone shall be dressed in the same way, eat the same food, read the book of the month, work at a belt. This is efficiency in contrast to the variety of life which one sees in Asia and in Europe. It is said that every American town looks like every other and that there is no need to see more than one. The same is true of the modern English suburb and garden city upon which a Frenchman passed epigrammatic judgment after being shown around one of them—"C'est une ville morte". That summed it up. It was spiritually dead. Even the army found that out, when at the beginning of the war the authorites eliminated regimental distinctions and made every one belong just to the army: a bad psychological mistake which was gradually rectified. Mass Production and the British Restaurant are not signs of progress in true civilisation but of retrogression as are many other aspects of planning. All of which does not imply that heaven is synonymous with chaos and anarchy.

Production goods, however, are much more independent of cultures. Drain pipes and water supplies whether in New York, Pekin, London or Delhi, are good ideas everywhere. They have, it might be noted, a double advantage that not only do they do more for health than all the doctors put together but they can be buried. Machines of all kinds for saving labour will be in demand irrespective of the type of living. It is interesting to watch what effect these new techniques have upon cultures and how they modify them. How long does East remain East with a really scientific education and a mechanised environment? People thought the Japanese had been westernised, though they never looked happy in frock coats, and so they were from certain points of view. They could build quite good liners and battle-ships but we found out a few things about them in the late war. Ways of thought change slowly and the spiritual subconscious mind more slowly. It is not economic geography but it might help in understanding Japan if one reads *The Chrysanthemum and the Sword* by Ruth Benedict. This is an anthropologist's study of the 'pattern of Japanese culture'. It gives food for thought.

Patterns of culture must be carefully distinguished from standards of living, the former are essentially non-material and spiritual, the latter are an economist's concept. The term standard of living can be used with various broader and narrower meanings but is usually taken to refer to material things and to certain patterns of living. Where money is stable in value it would be expressed in terms of money. Thus a man spending £800 a year would enjoy twice the standard as one spending £400. Wealth and welfare are not synonymous and much has been written on the relationship of the two. One speaks of a standard of living for the working class, for the middle and upper classes, though a little thought will warn one to be careful. When using such terms as a low standard or a high standard of living it is nearly always with reference to some definite standard in the speaker's or writer's mind. This standard should be made explicit. How difficult this can be will be seen in books dealing with such subjects.

Many people confuse income and welfare. It is true that in this country today if income falls below a certain sum for, say, a married couple with three children they will not be able to buy what we would call the bare necessaries of life, though these would demand definition. Rowntree in his classic study on poverty in York discusses this relationship between income and well-being. The book *Poverty* is still worth reading though it applies to a period now long past. 'Primary' poverty degrades in every sense but where, say, families have an income of £7 a week their welfare will vary much according as to how the money is spent.

Given a 'low' standard of living as we conceive it one can say that such people will exert little effective demand for goods. By effective demand the economist means demand backed by immediate purchasing power. Thus a starving man with no purchasing power has no demand for food. This sounds an immoral statement: it is merely a matter of the meaning of words and terms. The standard of the ordinary Indian peasant or workman is very low compared with ours, and this means that effective demand for goods is lacking. Thus it will be seen that one reason why production can be held up is because people cannot buy. They cannot buy because their production is low. The vicious circle is complete. It is in such cases that we can either resign ourselves as would an Oriental fatalist or classical economist, or do what? The modern economist does not think resignation is either wise or necessary. The fact, however, remains that a low standard of living implies a weak demand and that for inferior and cheap goods. It is not merely because the Indian cotton operative is unskilful that the greater part of the output of Indian cotton goods is in the lower counts. It is necessary to watch this reaction of lack of purchasing power upon the type and quality of goods produced. Then, too, in general, people with such standards, not knowing what good work is, tend to make poor work people easily satisfied and so again influence the quality of goods. A strong argument against allowing only utility goods to be sold in this country.

When considering standards one must be careful. There is no mathematical relationship between standards of living and of workmanship: witness much of the fine craftsmanship of the 18th century in this country. Standards of living as measured by our ideas were low. So it is too in Japan. Here are people who live on a totally different plane from ourselves. Attempts have been made from time to time to explain the Japanese success in the cotton industry by the fact that they lived under slum conditions. This is untrue. Whatever the Japanese may be they are not slum dwellers, though we could not tolerate the austerity of their living. That charge could have been made of the conditions in Bombay when the author saw them years ago. In such cases where high quality production is combined with simple and austere living it will be found that there is a strong moral quality in the cultural background.

These different standards in different countries will have a marked effect not only on the demand for and the supply of goods but must play a vastly important part in international trade and competition. On the international markets the competitive ability of a country will depend upon the efficiency of its labour. If the work people demand a high standard of living, which in itself is a perfectly right and laudable demand, they must back it by a high productivity. That is a relationship which is not well remembered in this country today, but sooner or later it must be. To what extent does raising incomes influence the urge to work? Economists at one time took it for granted that increased wages or salaries automatically called forth more effort. With primitive peoples it does not. Their standards are fixed by custom and a higher wage simply means that they will work less. It is the problem which faces one everywhere when primitive peoples are first brought into contact with modern industry. Often the labour will not come at all, the people preferring to stay in their villages. It is this which has led to the various policies and devices for bringing or forcing them out, poll taxes, forced labour and various administrative pressures all of which are gravely suspect and rightly so. Nevertheless in the past the problem was a real one. One might note in passing that conscription is a form of forced labour; 'direction' has a tinge of compulsion. Some form of pressure there will be until we become all-wise. Much depends upon how the pressure is applied though one is right to regard it with suspicion. Nor is this phenomenon of increased wages failing to induce the workmen to work harder and longer hours confined only to primitive peoples. It is obvious in our own country and throughout the West. As conditions improve part of the improvement is taken out in leisure. There is little to be said in favour of very long hours of work.

The Americans, however, have shown that high standards are compatible with competitive power. American exports are chiefly in those commodities in the manufacture of which high wages are paid.   This can be attributed to three major reasons: (1) American labour has always connected productivity and wages, a connection never clearly seen in this country, (2) behind the worker there is a much higher horse power and often superior machines and organisation, and (3) which is often forgotten, the American continent is vast and richly endowed so that Nature gives a bigger return even for the same effort.   The American miner produces much more coal than the British even when one has cleared away the misconceptions due to methods of compiling figures.   This is partly because it is easier to dig coal in the States than with us.

Finally we should note how doggedly people cling to their standards just as they do to their customs.   Circumstances may force a standard down but the pressure must be great and persistent.   It can happen.   This clinging to one's standards of living partly explains the irrational demands made in this country today, where all classes are resisting what need be only temporary reductions.   On the other hand the desire to raise standards of living is very obvious.   Some people are astonished how slowly standards are raised, but in this they display a double ignorance. First they fail to realise how much standards have been raised in the past half century; when people talk of austerity today many of their grandparents would laugh if they could hear them. Second they ignore the fact that to raise the standards of 50,000,000 as in these islands or of 400,000,000 as in India implies a vast demand on the world's resources of raw materials and power coupled with a capital supply which itself must be vastly great.   All this does not imply that standards cannot be raised but only that it will take time and work.   Unhappily not enough attention has been paid to improving the quality of consumption.   Welfare is not merely a matter of material goods.

CHAPTER V

APPROACH TO STUDY OF PRODUCTION:
AGRICULTURE AND MINING

ONE had originally called this chapter 'Techniques and changes in techniques of production,' but found that either the title must be misleading or one must write at least a volume describing techniques of all the major industries. Space forbids, even if one were capable of so doing, and on afterthoughts, one decided to treat the approach as when teaching a class. To take an analogy, it is rather like an older and more experienced tracker taking out a party of beginners and showing them what to look for and how to interpret the signs. Those who have read Bertram Thomas' *Arabia Felix* will remember how his Arab guide one day walking along a camel track told Thomas what kind of camel had plodded that way. From those apparently uninteresting marks in the sand the Arab could almost see the party which had recently passed by. So here one will try to act as the guide pointing to the things which seem to matter. The Arab could do this because he knew a lot about camels and their ways. We too ought to know a lot about techniques, the more the better. This chapter will tell you nothing about techniques, which you must get to know as you go along. It will not be systematic; just here and there points will be taken up to illustrate an idea.

There are innumerable books, a few of which will be suggested as one goes on, but good as books can be, they will not suffice. You must go and see. Visit farms, mines and factories, and talk to those who are running them if they will allow you to: not even watching is enough. At some time or other one must have done some steady work. A few of my pupils have been Bevin boys; it was a great education. The old Jews used to teach every boy a trade. St. Paul was a tent-maker and Christ was a carpenter. That's important to remember. If you want to be a fool, limit your studies to books.

I propose now to pick my subjects in a certain order: agriculture, mining and manufactures.

We speak of agriculture and of farmers, thinking like townsmen in a vague way, but that will not do for geographers who aim at accurate knowledge and statements, nor in fact will it do for the modern voting democrat who has the power through his vote to create or destroy.   If today public affairs are unsatisfactory, it is because the voting public has neither knowledge nor the desire for knowledge.   Power without knowledge and morals is as dangerous as the atom bomb.

When is a farmer, a farmer?   There is a book entitled *Farmers of Forty Centuries* by F. H. King, which deals with the Chinese farmer and his methods of cultivation.   It is an excellent book, well worth reading, though we need not read it all.   But are the mass of the Chinese cultivators farmers?   Certainly not in the English sense, we should call them peasants, and in fact much of their cultivation is more like horticulture than farming. Even peasants differ one from the other.   The better-to-do French, Danish and German peasants cultivating the larger holdings might be classified as small farmers, such as are found in many of the smaller 'family farms' of the U.S.   We must then be careful in our choice of words, but we ought to look at the size of the agricultural units in the various countries of the world.   We notice very soon that it is dangerous and misleading to talk of the average sized farm.   Let us take a few cases.

The United States.   There are according to the "Statistical Abstract"[1] 5,859,169 farms.   It would be as well to read the definition of a farm, or rather description.   Anything of three acres or above may be a farm;   also included 'are nurseries, greenhouses, hothouses, fur farms, mushroom cellars, apiaries and cranberry bogs.'   That is important for it helps us to understand the statement that 58% of the farmers were cultivating farms of less than 100 acres.   All these occupied only 11·4% of the total cultivated land.   It leaves 42% farming 100 acres upwards and that is a large number, actually 2,452,884 farms.   Of these, 286,676 were farms of 500 acres upwards occupying just over half the total farming land.   This is important, especially

[1] 1947, p. 590.

when we notice that farms of 1,000 acres and over occupied 40·3%
of the total land.   Here we have figures with which to begin to
make comparisons with the great State farms of Russia.   It
leaves in between the two extremes 2,166,208 farms about 40%
of the land area.   These form the great core of the 'family farms.'
It is obvious then that we cannot just talk of farming in the U.S.
as if farms are all pretty much alike.   This is a beginning.   We
now listen to Mr. H. R. Tolley, or rather we read the paper
which he read to the Fourth International Conference of Agricultural Economists in 1936.   It is published by O.U.P.   Much
of it ought to be reproduced verbatim here as it is already compressed, and I commend it to my readers.   He starts by a sketch
of the variations in the farming systems of the U.S., due to
geographical environment.   Here the reader is reminded that
all our studies pre-suppose the required background which at
times must be contemplated.   Here is what he says: I venture
to quote at some length both because of the excellence of the
description itself and as an example of how such a subject should
be approached.

"Owing to the wide expanse of territory and to the varied
physical, topographic, climatic, and economic conditions
prevailing, there are few, if any, countries in the world with
a more diverse agriculture than is to be found in the United
States.   Although there is a wide diversity in the kinds and
varieties of agricultural products grown, there are, in fact,
fairly distinct patterns in which the different regions and areas
combine these different enterprises into farming systems.
"The number of such areas that may be differentiated
obviously will be determined by the degree of refinement
desired.   The agriculture of the United States can be divided
into 12 major agricultural regions and into 100 sub-regions.
Certain of these regions, such as the Corn Belt of the Middle
West, the Cotton Belt of the South, the Wheat and Small
Grain Regions in the Great Plains, the Range Livestock
Region in the Mountain and Great Basin States, the Dairy
Region of the Lake and North Eastern States, are concen-
trated in clearly defined and contiguous geographic centres;

others, such as the Fruit and Mixed Farming, Truck and Special Crops Regions, represent several scattered but clearly defined local type-of-farming areas. When combined these comprise a group of areas that have problems essentially similar in character.

"In the Middle West, for example, is found the Great Corn Belt of the United States. Throughout the region the land is level with deep, warm, black soils, rich in lime, nitrogen, and organic material. These soils are remarkably fertile and, when associated as they are with high day and night temperatures, ample rainfall, and a reasonably long growing season, are almost ideal for the production of corn. Although corn is the most important crop, oats, barley, wheat, and hay are also important, with the small grains being sown in the fall after corn cultivation is over and before harvesting is started, thus serving as excellent nurse crops for getting the hay and pasture crops established.

"The feed grains and hay produced in the Corn Belt are largely marketed through live stock. Approximately 75% of the hogs commercially slaughtered in the United States are produced in the Corn Belt and closely associated General Farming Region. The great bulk of the grain-fed cattle coming to market are also fed in the Corn Belt.

"North of the Corn Belt, and in the North-east, where the climate is cooler and the soils not so rich as in the Corn Belt, the land is better adapted to small grains, hay and pasture, rather than corn; and this, together with the fact that a large urban population is located in or close to the area, has resulted in the development of the Dairy Region.

"Cotton is the important crop in the Cotton Belt of the South. The northern boundary of the cotton crop, which is a sub-tropical crop requiring a relatively high temperature which increases through the growing season, is largely determined by the northern limit of the 200-day growing season, while the western boundary is determined by the line of 20-inch annual rainfall. Cotton is the chief crop in the South because of its exacting climate requirements, and because a large supply of relatively low-priced labour is available in the form of a dense negro population. In addition to cotton most farmers in the South endeavour to grow enough corn to supply cornmeal for home use and feed for work stock.

"Cotton, however, does not get first choice of the land throughout the South. Tobacco is as exacting as cotton from the standpoint of climate and is much more exacting with respect to soil. On the sandy soils in the eastern and south-eastern coastal plain, flue-cured tobacco is the chief cash crop, and this area, together with the burley and fire-cured tobacco areas in Kentucky and Tennesse, make up the Tobacco and General Farming Region.

"The General Farming Region between the cotton and tobacco sections of the South and the Corn Belt of the North is a transition region in which no one enterprise is dominant. Corn, hay and small grains are important crops and live stock, including poultry and sheep, are found throughout the region.

"The important wheat regions are the Hard Winter Wheat Region centring in Kansas, the Hard Spring Wheat Region in North and South Dakota and Montana, and the Soft Wheat Region in the Pacific North-west. Thus they are located on the level Great Plains and in the level to rolling Pacific North-west where large fields, relatively dry soils and level lands are favourable also to the use of large-scale machinery, which means low costs, even though only low or moderate yields are obtained. The improvement in machinery, especially the development of the combine and tractor, together with a relatively good market demand and several years of above-normal rainfall in the decade ending about 1930, resulted in a rather rapid westward expansion of wheat growing in the Great Plains, with the result that a considerable acreage of marginal and sub-marginal land was brought under cultivation. Grain sorghums are the chief feed-grain crop in the Hard Winter Wheat Region, while barley, rye and flax are important crops in the Hard Spring Wheat Region.

"The Range Live-Stock Region of the United States is located in the arid and semi-arid West. The region, which extends from the Flint Hills in Kansas to the Pacific Coast and from the mesquite grass and coastal ranges in southern Texas to the plains of northern Montana, is a great breeding ground for feeder and grass-fat cattle, and for sheep. All types of ranges are included, and since practically none of it can be cultivated, it must be utilized by the grazing animals, usually cattle or sheep, although goats are occasionally important. There are irrigated valleys and small dry-farming areas located throughout the range region, which usually produce hay and some grain which is used for winter feed" (pages 228–30).

That is by no means all, but it is enough for our purpose. There can be no neat one-paragraph approach to so vast a subject. Now we are ready to ask what techniques do these millions of farmers employ; are they all highly mechanised and all run on highly scientific lines? Tolley refers to this; he points out that mechanisation has progressed at different rates in different parts of the country, and that it has developed fastest in areas with level land, where farmers have a reasonable amount of capital and credit and where new blocks of land are being brought into cultivation. It is all very well summed up in the following quotation taken from *World Agriculture* published by the Royal Institute of International Affairs, 1932.

"Mechanisation has not yet been applied in all districts or in all branches of the industry. Maize and cotton crops are still mainly dependent on hand labour, though changes are taking place in these branches of agriculture also. Even in cotton-growing, machinery is making great headway in Texas and Oklahoma and, where employed, has increased human efficiency from ten- to twenty-fold in certain operations. On light, dry, soil cereal-growing, with the aid of the tractor and the combine, allows a greatly increased output per man. The man with the oil-can is replacing the man with the spade. Agriculture is regarded as an industry which must be organized to secure the highest production with the minimum of labour, to spend capital lavishly on machinery, and to secure a quick return on capital. This means a dis-

placement of labour and a gradual approximation of American agriculture to the conditions of other industries.   It
implies larger capital charges and smaller expenditure on
labour.   The methods of industrialism are being applied
to agriculture.   Just as the industrial revolution of the
nineteenth century began with English inventors and the
English development of the factory system, so the agricultural revolution of the twentieth century has been largely
due to American development of the 'mechanized prairie
farm,' with its mechanical tools of production, its packing
departments, and its organized marketing" (page 114).

Nevertheless much of the development has been unhealthy
and no one is more aware than the American that much of the
farming in the U.S. has been of the nature of land mining, and
that it has not really been farming at all.   Here, perhaps, one
might digress.   There is no doubt that in the new Worlds of
America and Australia cultivators have approached their job
from a totally different angle to that of, say, the British farmer or
the Mediterranean peasant.   Land was in abundance, the whole
world was on the move and the race for wealth made men impatient and reckless.   The results can be seen in the grave losses
by erosion everywhere.   Let us take the U.S. figures which can
be found in *Soils and Men*[1]—a magnificent book for reference.
The article in particular is "General Aspects of the Soil-erosion
Problem."   The figures given are staggering and only a vast
country such as the United States could survive such losses.
The total farm area is 1,141,615,000 acres, of which 352,866,000[2]
are cropland.   Here are the figures:—

Total land area
      Ruined or severely damaged   282,000,000 acres
      Moderately damaged   775,000,000   ,,
Cropland
      Ruined for cultivation   50,000,000   ,,
      Severely damaged   50,000,000   ,,

[1] U.S. Department of Agriculture, 1938.
[2] 1945.

Cropland

One half of all top soil gone	100,000,000 acres
Erosion process beginning	100,000,000 ,,

That cannot go on indefinitely and already the Americans have begun to tackle the problem.   It is, however, vast, and feeding Europe is directing attention to production and away from conservation.   In Great Britain during the 19th century farm leases were drawn with great severity.   It was clearly laid down what the farmer could and could not do; what he could take off the land and what he had to put into it.   These leases have been considered by the ignorant as merely obstructive documents. Maybe they were sometimes too rigid but they aimed at conserving the fertility of the land.   So in the Mediterranean lands with their thin soils and many slopes.   Much of the cultivator's time is taken up in preventing soil erosion and in conserving fertility.   This conservation work has raised costs of production and so placed the British and Mediterranean cultivators at a disadvantage with the American or Canadian farmer in the markets.   That is far from being the whole picture, but it is an important bit.   Good farming must aim at leaving the land in, at least, as good condition as when cultivation began.   In their turn, the authorities and better farmers in the U.S. are now aiming at good farming and many new methods are being experimented with.

Much of what has been said of the U.S. would apply equally well to Australia, Canada, South Africa, though each of these countries has its special problem.   Let us now look at the other extreme in the East, which is well typified in Japan, China and India.   In Japan only 15·8% of the country is available for cultivation.   The density per cultivated square mile is about 432, so that competition for land is intense.   Of the holdings, 49·37% were under 1·25 acres; 24·2% between 1·25 and 2·45 acres, making practically 75% less than 3 acres.   Holdings over 25 acres were roughly 1%.   Rice is the dominant crop, making nearly 54% of the total crop values.   This is not farming in our sense; it is Asiatic peasant agriculture or horticulture. The Japanese Government in the past 70 years has done much to increase output and to help the peasants by making roads, by seed selection and facilitating the fertiliser supply, but, as one writer has put it, nothing has been done to alter the framework within which agriculture functions. It is the laborious, careful cultivation so well known in the Far East. Given the size of the holdings, the fact that there is little level ground so that large fields would be impossible and the relative poverty of the culti- vator, improved techniques through the employment of machin- ery are almost impossible. Statistics show that the incomes of the peasantry have not risen in proportion to that of the rest of the nation and that there was much real poverty even for Japan. Indeed Japanese agriculture was made possible by the intense thrift and laboriousness of the Japanese cultivator class; by additional income received through the earnings of younger members of the family in industry and in many cases by the earnings from silk production. It was a type of cultivation which admitted of little further amelioration or expansion. The most optimistic estimate was that of all land which could be improved and cultivated, 80% was already used. This rigid limitation of Japanese agriculture had important repercussions in the industrial development of the nation.

China presents the same picture, only made more unpleasant by chronic civil war and by foreign invasion. Here the Mal- thusian checks have been only too obvious in making the popu- lation fit the food supply. India presents much the same pic- ture, though there is considerable variation, especially in the more newly settled canal colonies. In all three countries the outstanding fact is the complete lack of what we would call farm capital. Yet outwardly to the tourist the picture can be pleasing and even beautiful. The terraced hill-sides following the contours command admiration, but such terracing always implies poverty of good level land, and therefore human poverty. The rice fields with their wonderful fresh green can be a delight, but one which is not long without qualification. Nor, indeed, can one who knows these people, withhold admiration for their patience, thrift and cheerfulness; but theirs is a technique which has definite limits. Given a stationary population of, say, one-third present numbers, the cultivators might be rela- tively prosperous—at least by Eastern European standards.

Lastly we might glance at our own country, taking A. W. Menzies-Kitchen's little book *The Future of British Farming* as a guide and a very excellent one, too. Two warnings, first that you cannot give a complete picture outside an encyclopaedia, and second, as Sir E. V. Russell, one of our greatest authorities, has written in warning: "No country in the world has such wide variations of soil and climate compacted into so narrow a range as Great Britain. In consequence, British agriculture is exceedingly varied and it is the most difficult in the world to dogmatise about." I imagine that every authority in every country would say the same thing; nevertheless it is true. If you cannot read the whole of Menzies-Kitchen, read the chapter, "Economic Characteristics". Here you will find a table giving the number of agricultural holdings by size. The author in his commentary writes: "It will be seen that in 1937 only 3·2 per cent of the holdings were over 300 acres in size, and only 12·4 per cent were above 150 acres. Therefore approximately 87 per cent of the farmers of this country are farming 150 acres or less, while 79 per cent have holdings of not more than 100 acres. . . . Farmers with 150 acres or less, however, only occupy 49 per cent of the land, the other 51 per cent being held by the remaining 13 per cent of farmers." It is upon the size of the farm and its modern equipment that so much depends, but there is more in it than that. Table IX has an interesting analysis of Gross Income by Size Group. Space will not permit one to say more. One can only suggest a few additional books, such as *Economics of Peasant Farming* by Warriner, which gives a good survey of peasant farming in Europe. This is academic in its approach. *Peasant Europe* by H. Hessell Tiltman is not academic, but neither is the life of a peasant, especially in Eastern Europe. For China there is a recently published book *Earthbound China* by Hsaio-Tung Fei and Chi-I Chang. This is quite a large book and deals specifically with Yunnan. For India there are hosts of books, but M. L. Darling's three books on the Punjab are outstanding. One only I will mention, *The Punjab Peasant*. What Darling didn't know about the Punjab wasn't worth knowing, but better still, he had an affection for him. This is at least as important as statistics. For our own country again the difficulty is one of choice. Mine is purely arbitrary and one might equally recommend others. *This Farming Business* by Frank Sykes, a farmer who made his farm pay! *The Farm in the Fen* by Alan Bloom describes the reclaiming of a derelict fen farm and brings out some of the peculiar difficulties of such farms; *The Farming Ladder* by George Henderson, tells of the small farm: all three are excellent and make pleasant reading, apart from their scientific value. Miss R. Cohen's *Economics of Agriculture* in the Cambridge Economic Handbooks, gives a straightforward and good account of the economic organisation behind the farm and the farmer. There is a Penguin Special, *Ley Farming* by Sir R. George Stapledon and William Davies, and a Pelican, *British Agriculture* by Viscount Astor and B. Seebohm Rowntree. Both these are excellent, though the latter is controversial. One does not expect the reader to read all these books, but he might read one or two and just glance at some of the others.

Let us now sum up before we pass on to mining. Food is fundamental to all life, be it primitive or highly civilised, and the methods of obtaining it vary equally much. Even among the civilised peoples techniques vary immensely according to the nature of the environment, the historical background, the science and capital available, and the enterprise of the cultivators. As a result the productivity per worker varies immensely and this not only determines his standard of living but affects that of the non-agriculturalists. It is reckoned that probably 70 to 75% of the world's population is engaged in producing food, yet food supplies are inadequate and always have been, both in quantity and quality. This obviously sets a great part of the economic pattern for the world though one hesitates here to use the word pattern. Taking the world as a whole it is a patchwork of local patterns all of which must be examined with care. Which is the best? The question cannot be put in that way. We have seen the disastrous results of some of the American 'advanced' techniques in the 'Dustbowl': on the other hand one has only to study the smaller French peasant or the Indian ryot at work to realise how soul-destroying can be the petty economies and exaggerated thrift of the really poor cultivator literally wringing a bare sustenance out of a reluctant and sterile soil. Guy de Maupassant depicts this in many of his bitter stories which are worth reading, and the writer can corroborate what he writes. This bitter penury kills all the human traits and makes men and women greedy, savage and cruel and is true of all peasantries under such conditions. But not all peasants are like that: the better ones can live quite full lives and be happy. Indeed they lead fuller lives than most of the modern town dwellers for the peasant is living with realities and can see the full circle of the year and of life, while the modern townsman lives an ersatz life often working on a belt and filling up his spare time at a cinema. One must study each type of cultivator and always with relation to his full background.

If man cannot live without food, modern man cannot live without a great abundance and variety of minerals. Our civilisation is based and built up on metals and power. Take these away and it must collapse. Everyone knows this, but like many familiar things, it passes unnoticed. One needs to be constantly aware of it (1) when reading history, for the past civilisations were evolved without either power or the use of metals as we understand use. This must be remembered when making comparisons with the past as recently as a hundred years ago or even less; (2) when considering the greater part of the world's people even today. Except for Japan, and India to a slight extent, the Asiatic peoples lack both power and metals; so in Africa as a whole (though South Africa is an exception) and in South Eastern Europe. Differences in national wealth turn largely upon the presence or absence of metals and power; (3) modern war cannot be waged without a superabundance of metal. Hence the eagerness with which modern peoples search for minerals and strive to obtain control over them. It has just been remarked that minerals are the great factor in our civilisation, but such a statement must be interpreted in its functional relationship to our modern life. Mining supplies the raw materials upon which the metallurgical industries are based, but modern mining would be impossible without modern science, while metallurgy has created demands for the rarer metals.

Our first concern ought to be that of finding out how the

world's minerals are distributed, that is, as far as we know. Of course we do not know too much and the reader is advised to take estimates as estimates and not as firm figures. All estimates are based upon specified conditions, which should be known to the reader. Instead of estimates we might take actual production figures, which are quite definite. Which is the better method depends upon what we are trying to do. If, for instance, we are considering what will be the coal output for this country during the next five years, the actual output of coal over the past twenty years is a better guide to what can be done than, say, Dr. Strahan's estimate of total reserves as 178,727 million tons. That his figures do not quite tally with those of Professor H. S. Jevons, is neither here nor there. If, however, we are looking forward, say, fifty years, as a wise people should, then some of these estimates become vastly important. It is obvious that Great Britain with its limited mineral supplies could not compete in outputs with the U.S., whose coal-fields are of greater extent than the whole of the British Isles. For many purposes it is immediately available resources that matter.

Here may I suggest books. There are two useful Pelicans—*Minerals in Industry* by W. R. Jones, and *Metals* by Alexander and Street. These are easily available. Two most useful books, both American, are *World Minerals and World Peace* by Leith, Furness and Lewis, and *From the Ground Up* by Paul M. Tyler.[1] The former gives in a straightforward and simple way all the important facts and is especially good in the use of diagrams and maps. The maps are particularly helpful. Among other things it deals with attempts to control mineral supplies through cartels, and by means of national policies. The latter deals more with the actual mining methods in the U.S., and there are chapter dealing with most metals that matter. It is most readable and helpful. I have gone to both these books for some of my facts. The *Minerals Year Book* published by the U.S. Bureau of Mines has 1,500 pages of information and is a magnificent piece of work. Another equally good—*The Mineral Industry* is issued by

[1] The Brookings Institute, 1943, and the McGraw-Hill Book Co., 1948, respectively.

the McGraw-Hill Book Company.   This is by far the most comprehensive unofficial work of its kind and should be known to
all.   Bain *Ores and Industry in the Far East* is an authoritative
work for that region.   He also has one on South America.
Finally, every Handbook has good chapters on metals.   The
difficulty is not lack of material, but its superabundance.   All
we can do here is to consider a very few examples and even these
must be treated superficially.   We are using them merely as
examples of how to read signs and interpret them.   If knowledge
is wanted, the reader must refer to some of the reading just
mentioned.

Let us begin with coal.   The *League of Nations Year Book*[1]
gives a table for the whole world for the years 1929 to 1938
inclusive.   It does this for all the leading minerals and is by far
the most accessible compilation.   It would seem better if we
could have the figures for 1945 but they are not published yet,
and they would not actually serve our purpose as the war period
is too abnormal and upset; nor, in fact, is this period 1929–38
an ideal one, but we will make do, as it will be useful for showing
how to get to work.   We are trying to get a bird's-eye view of
world production and the relative importance of the continents
and individual countries.   For this purpose 1929 gives, on the
whole, a better picture for Europe, but not the best for the other
continents, for which we will take 1937 or 1938 as the figures are
available.   Here then is the composite picture:

Africa	14,545,000	tons (metric)	1929
America, North	564,582,000	,, ,,	,,
America, Central	1,054,000	,, ,,	,,
America, South	2,216,000	,, ,,	,,
Asia	111,000,000	,, ,,	1937
U.S.S.R.	132,000,000	,, ,,	1938
Europe (less U.S.S.R.)	605,725,000	,, ,,	1929
Oceania	13,254,000	,, ,,	1938

The dominating positions of Europe and North America stand
out especially if one remembers that much of the U.S.S.R. coal

[1] 1938/39.

D

is European mined, and we are interested to know why this should be so. Take the four great producers for 1938:—

	Coal	Population
U.S.A.	352,000,000 tons	130,000,000
U.K.	231,000,000 ,,	47,000,000
Germany	186,000,000 ,,	68,000,000
U.S.S.R.	133,000,000 ,,	169,000,000
Total	902,000,000 ,,	414,000,000
World Total	1,225,000,000 ,,	2,126,000,000

These four countries produced, roughly, three-quarters of the world's coal, but had only one-fifth the world's population. It might be just luck that these countries possessed the coal, and to a considerable extent this is true. The Swedish output of 431,000 tons can hardly be attributed to the lack of enterprise or backwardness of the Swedes. We do know, in fact, that these mining countries and regions are the most richly endowed. There is nothing comparable in the southern hemisphere which produces less than 3% of the world's coal and oil and which has less than 2% of the world's iron and steel industry. It is not all luck, however. China is known to possess great coal deposits, though in the past they were exaggerated, as today they are probably under-estimated, yet China's maximum production was 21,000,000 tons in 1934, and even if we add in the Manchurian output of 14,000,000 tons (1937), the total for that vast country is only 35,000,000 tons. The explanation lies fundamentally in the lack of modern techniques—(1) the lack of the great technique of keeping law and order; (2) lack of a modern transport system; (3) lack of mining techniques which make the Chinese rely upon foreign advisers, with all the difficulties which arise therefrom. The Indian production for 1938 was under 20,000,000—a bagatelle for so vast a country. Here again it is not lack of coal as will be revealed in the reports on Indian mining.

Mines vary enormously in size and output, so that generalisation is dangerous.   These days, when size and speed are the two great gods, it is well to be warned, because only too often they can be false ones.   That efficiencies can be improved almost everywhere is beyond question, but the methods are open to discussion.   Take the U.S. mines as a first example, as the U.S. is the greatest producer and as it leads the world in size and techniques:—

NUMBER AND SIZE OF BITUMINOUS MINES, 1942

Outputs Tons	No. of mines	% of total	Average output per mine-Tons	% of total	
500,000+	316	4·5	888,000	48·2	74·6 output
2–500,000+	495	7·1	311,000	26·4	11·6 mines
1–200,000	484	6·9	145,000	12·0	
50,000–100,000	445	6·4	71,500	5·5	
10–50,000	1,492	21·4	22,400	5·7	7·9 output
10,000 —	3,740	53·7	3,500	2·2	75·1 mines
Total	6,972	100	83,600	100	

Total output 582,700,000 tons.

The figures are astonishing.   11·6% of the mines produce 75% of the total output of bituminous coal; that is what we would expect.   The astonishment comes when one contemplates 75% of the mines producing just under 8% of the coal, and that there should be 5,232 mines with averages varying between 22,400 and 3,500 tons.   All the bituminous mines employed 457,000 men, a much smaller number than are employed in this country.   Efficiency has been increasing, for in 1923 there were 11,715 mines employing 705,000 men producing roughly the same amount, 564,000,000 tons.   The rise in the output per worker is very evident.   Tyler, in his book, says that between 1939–44 there was an increase in output per man of 73%.   The average output per worker is about 5½ tons in the bituminous mines, and 3 in the anthracite.   How far is this due to Nature's bounty, how much to efficiency of organisation, and how much to the men?   These are important questions for the economic geographer and must always be asked. Partly it is Nature's bounty. Mining in the U.S. is a simple matter compared with the U.K. There the deepest mines are not more than 1,000 ft., while the average is about 260. Less than a quarter of the mines have shafts, being approached by horizontal 'drifts' or downward slopes, or they are strip mines. Forty per cent of the bituminous coal comes from seams of 6 ft. or more in thickness and only 19% from seams of less than 4 ft. Timbering is less necessary owing to the strong roofs, while the seams are less faulted. There is no doubt, too, that in the larger mines techniques have been steadily improved. During the war the efficiency in using labour was also greatly improved. Given these two factors it is not easy to know how much is due to the miner himself and we should be wise to withhold judgment until we knew more. What, of course, is obvious is that the wealth production per head is greater and so real wages can be higher, and this affects the consuming power of the miners. We might quote the paragraph from Tyler just to show that we are not the only ones with our troubles:

"From 1939 to 1944, a 57 per cent gain in output of bituminous coal—from 395 to 620 million tons—was made in spite of a 9 per cent drop in the number of men employed—from 422,000 to 383,000. The annual output per man increased 73 per cent—in part as the result of increased output per manday, but largely because of the increase in number of days worked per year. Lack of all-year markets, with attendant seasonal unemployment, has always characterised bituminous-coal mining. The insistent demand for coal during the war made full employment possible. . . . At the same time, however, the labour force deteriorated, so that many workers were unable to take advantage of the opportunity simply because they lacked the necessary physical stamina. A large proportion of the younger, more vigorous yet well-trained men left the coal mines for the armed services or went into other industries, with the result that an abnormally large proportion of coal miners on the job were men over fifty. Absenteeism which increased as earnings went up, was partly due also to the fact that men in these higher age brackets were physically incapable of arduous underground toil on the basis of the expanded hours of work day after day."

How efficient was, and is, our own coal mining industry? That must be a matter for dispute, but as geographers and economists we might note certain facts. These will be found in very considerable detail in the "Report on the Coal Industry, 1925,[1]" which is very fact-finding and dispassionate. Read particularly Chapter V: 'Structure of the Industry,' The P.E.P. Report, "British Fuel and Power Industries," gives a good short view to 1947. This will probably be suspect by many but it is factual. The tables are as useful as any short tables can be. The coal mining industry, as a national problem, long ceased to be economic and is a psychological one, but even the psycho-analyst searches for the causes of phobias.

The Commission reported that in 1924 there were some 2,481 mines operated by 1,400 companies but that 98% of the output was produced by 715 companies and 84% by 323 undertakings, each employing over 1,000 persons. If we take the war period— 1939 to 1944—our output, unlike the American, has gone steadily down from 231 to 192 millions, and if we ask the same three questions the answers are not all so good. Nature is not so bountiful; that has been shown already; moreover, we have been working our mines for a longer time. Organisation calls for hot dispute. Now at least the figures show that mechanisation was begun before 1935 when 51% of the coal was cut by machinery; in 1944 it was 72%. For the same years conveyancer machinery handled 43% and 71% respectively. There is much more to it than that. As to the human factor much can be said for and against. The man in the street cannot know and must go to the experts. One does know, however, what the absentee percentage is. Few would assert that British coal-mining is efficient or satisfactory for whatsoever cause, though there unanimity ends. Again, however, one fact stands out, the actual productivity of the industry and the numbers em-

[1] Cmd. 2600.

ployed. Compared with the U.S., productivity is very low. That must effect the national dividend directly and indirectly as well as the wages and consuming power of the miners.

We must leave it at that. The European mining conditions approximate more to ours than the U.S. Perhaps one might add that in mining the new countries are at a great advantage in lay-out. Whatever our Coal Board may wish to do, however wise it may be, its long distance plans must be superimposed upon mining areas already torn about by more than a century of heavy mining. These plans must be developed while short period demands are being satisfied at the same time. The patient must not die during the operation.

Coal is the equivalent of power, so that we should pay attention not only to the quantity but to the quality. Coal experts do not talk of coal just like that. There are as many kinds of coal as there are tea, and each kind has its particular use: good coking coal is relatively rare and we have some of the best. The coal in the neighbourhood of Pittsburg is, or was, very good. As good coking coal is scarce, new techniques of mixing and coking have been developed which make it possible to use coal which would have been useless a generation ago. So with bad and inferior coals which used to be thrown away; many new methods such as pulverisation make them available. Forty years ago the amount of power available for industry could have been measured pretty accurately by the amount of coal available. Today in many countries this is far from being the case. Oil and electricity have been added. There is a good chapter on the petroleum industry in *Fundamentals of Economic Geography* by Bengtson and van Royen, still another American book, and Bain has a chapter. When dealing with electricity remember that only hydro-electricity is a new source of power. Thermo-electricity is only coal or oil. It is interesting to note how hydro-electricity has augmented the industrialisation of such countries as Switzerland and Sweden. Note also that each new source of power tends to have special adaptions or particular uses. Oil has not so much ousted coal as made a new field for itself, in transport especially by road and air, though it has taken the place of coal at sea very largely. In this country the electric power in the factories and works is only coal, with a few exceptions. It has been said that the development of hydro-electricity was causing another industrial revolution. This is an exaggeration as a general statement, though it may be true of certain countries.

If now one turns to that most precious of all metals, iron, one finds that it is very unequally distributed by Nature, both as to quantity and quality. The *League of Nations Year Book* gives the best quick view of world production of iron ore, but omits to tell us the amount of iron content. Iron content is vastly important from the point of view of wealth production. The U.S. ores are generally about 60% iron; the English certainly not more than half that amount. For a given effort then the Englishman can have only half the amount of income as the American. English ores were always poor, with a few exceptions. Even in 1889 the general percentage was only 35·6 as compared with nearly double from the imported ores. The percentage has slowly fallen as we have been driven to the inferior ores, and must be somewhat below 30% now. Here is a disability which must be faced though we escape by importing better class ores.

The purity of the ore matters. The Bessemer process of steel making at first demanded ores free from phosphorus, and the French minette ores were useless until the Thomas Gilchrist technique found a way of eliminating the phosphorus. There are other impurities such as sulphur which must be got rid of. How the ore is obtained is important for cost is ultimately a determining factor in production. Open pits are cheaper to mine than underground workings. In the States 72·5% of the ores comes from open pits where it is quarried on a vast scale. There is a very useful account of all these matters in *Minerals in Industry*.

The position of the mines will affect transport costs. It is the relative position of the materials, one to the other, that matters, but it is well to remember that the distance from the Lake Superior ores to Pittsburg is greater than that from the north coast of Spain to the South Wales blast furnaces. The Americans have minimised distance by their high techniques in handling ores and fuel, whether by water or land. We have nothing like it.   We, too, have the advantage of water transport when importing the better ores.

Two major raw materials are needed for the iron and steel industry—we have not space here to deal with the lesser ones—good coking coal and iron ore.   Given the present world where power politics has got badly muddled up with economics, it is better to have both these materials within the same political frontier.   Prior to 1914 it didn't matter nearly so much, nor is it fatal even today as we ourselves know, though it can be an embarrassment and a danger.   The U.S. have these two materials in vast amount and of high quality.   The U.S.S.R. most probably have them too.   The possible Western European Union would also be well endowed though the individual countries may have one or the other, or even both, to a limited extent.   In the modern world which aims at mass production and is ever threatened with war, everything turns on these basic materials.   Let us make a comparison between two extremes—the U.S. and China.   It will not be a waste of time and it may help in showing how to prognosticate a country's possible development and future well-being.

In 1942 the U.S. mined 105,500,000 tons of iron ore.   This dropped to 90,000,000 in 1945.   In the past one could gauge the steel output from the pig iron production, but the two are not so closely related owing to the use of scrap.   Steel making capacity in 1945 was about 95 million tons.   How can China compare with this?   When forecasting Chinese economic development, after supposing internal peace and a good single government, could we expect some comparable development given time, say, 70 years?   Seventy years ago U.S. production of pig iron was 2,300,000 tons; seventy years is about the time the Japanese had for their spectacular transformation and development.   The answer is very definitely no.   Bain quotes Tegengren's figures which he summarises.   The actually available ore is, roughly, 400,000,000 tons with a potential reserve of 560,000,000.   The total metallic content is 166,000,000 and 202,000,000 tons respectively, making a total of 368,000,000 tons.   Not much for 400,000,000 people if they wish to emulate the U.S.   It means that the future development of China will have to be on lines like that of Japan rather than of the U.S. or Western Europe. It will be a quiet, thrifty development. Experts do not think any spectacular iron discoveries are likely to be made in China, and they are probably right, though we should remember India where the great discoveries were made just when hope of large finds had been abandoned.

Let us now turn for a moment to that least of all useful metals, gold. That it is so, is proved by the decline in production after 1940. The U.S. issued a closing order at a time when everything was being done to increase the production of other metals. Output in the U.S. fell to one-fifth, and would have fallen even more had not a considerable part of the U.S. gold output been a by-product of such metals as copper and zinc. Gold is more than a metal; it is a myth. In this it is like the precious gems for which even comparatively decent men will commit crime. Gold has some uses in industry but they are slight; its major use is a monetary one, while the second use is for ornaments. World output in 1940 was roughly 42,000,000 ozs. While it is measured in ounces, most of the 'scarce' metals are measured in pounds. Forty-two million ounces is not much; it would aver- age about one-tenth of an ounce for each person in India, not enough to make a ring. Divided among the world's population it is roughly one-third of a pennyweight. After that one can only advise the reader to visit a goldsmith and ask to see what a pennyweight looks like. This emphasis is not a waste of time; one ought to know. The industry reveals one of the curious human traits. Thousands of men equipped with expensive capital goods toil to extract gold from the bowels of the earth in various parts of the world, while hundreds equally heavily equipped build elaborate strong boxes in which to bury this hard-won gold. Everybody is happy and all think they are better off. No wonder Lord Keynes said it was barbaric, but, as has been remarked already, we are barbarians.

The great producer is still South Africa, whose economy largely turns on the gold mining industry. Gold mining is to the South African what coal mining is to us. The estimate made by the Low Grade Ore Commission (V.G. 16. 32) was that one half of the people in South Africa obtain their livelihood directly

D*

or indirectly from the gold mining industry, and that half of the Government revenue comes directly or indirectly from the same source. How fine a business gold mining is, can be seen from the average amount of gold per ton of rock. It is only 4·2 dwt. Such an industry is only possible, given modern scientific techniques. Of Russian production we know little, but suspect that it is largely placer gold.

So we could go on. Tyler has a section headed, "A bewildering array", but the reader can take courage for in the last paragraph he writes:

"Almost as amazing as the profusion of elements and alloys, however, is the fact that only about ten metals bulk large enough in tonnage or dollar value to appear commercially significant to the statistician. Except for iron and the major non-ferrous metals, copper, lead and zinc, plus the currency metals, gold and silver, about the only elements that we can class as common metals are the newly important light metals, aluminium and magnesium, and perhaps nickel and tin. All the rest are frequently dealt with for most practical purposes as rare metals, even though many of them, in terms of known abundance in the earth's crust, are not really as rare as some of the so-called 'common' metals."

Enough has been said and now we must examine some other tracks and guess the nature of the beast which made them.

CHAPTER VI

APPROACH TO STUDY OF PRODUCTION:
MANUFACTURING INDUSTRY

IF it is difficult to discuss agriculture and mining, it is infinitely
more so manufacture. That is why we economic geographers tend to slur it over. For instance, how can one compress
into half a dozen lectures or a few chapters such a complex of
activities as we have in this country? If it were possible, even
then Great Britain is only one of many countries. Both teacher
and student are perplexed how to start and how to do the
pruning. There is no doubt that we should read some purely
descriptive books, such as *British Industries and their Organisation*
by G. C. Allen, which gives a bird's-eye view. It is curious how
few up-to-date books of this kind there are; one has to go to
reports when one can get them. What we need today is something equivalent to the "Reports of the Committee on Industry
and Trade," commonly called the Balfour Reports, published in
the late twenties, which, by-the-way, give excellent accounts with
statistics up to practically the great slump in 1929. They also
give very useful accounts of foreign developments. Some of
the "Working Party Reports" do supply this want, though these
reports vary very much, not only in size but in quality. Those
on Cotton and Wool are outstandingly good. Serious readers
should look at them, though all are warned that they take a good
deal of reading. All these reports are too advanced for the
general reader, who should turn to the geography text books
such as Dudley Stamp's *Intermediate Commercial Geography* or
Fundamentals of Economic Geography by Bengston and van Royen.
The last is an American book and is very up to date. These
books deal with the general distribution of industry and often
sketch briefly the techniques. For Germany as it was before the
war, there is C. W. Guillebaud's book, *The Economic Recovery of
Germany* 1933–38, and also a D.O.T. Report No. 641 of 1936—
"Economic Conditions in Germany". These between them give

a very adequate review of German industry and organisation and provide a background against which to do one's present day thinking. For France there is a voluminous D.O.T. Report No. 581 of 1934 which is very comprehensive. The Monnet Report I do not commend here.

While a good descriptive knowledge is desirable, and even necessary, it is not enough for our purpose, which is to take a survey of a country's activities and then of world activity. We are driven to statistics and these, as we know, are only useful when carefully compiled and fairly elaborate. All that one can acquire in this way is a superficial knowledge which can be exceedingly dangerous. Some time or other one is compelled to specialise by taking some one country and some one industry as types for detailed study. For our own country, readers can consult *The British Isles* by Stamp and Beaver, which is pretty thorough. For the U.S. there is a large tome published by Pitman's, *The Development of American Industries* edited by Glover and Cornell. The individual industries are each written up by a specialist; it is worth while looking at a few. Beginners would be better advised to take some such book as *North America* by Rodwell Jones and Bryan. All the Year Books, too, have good chapters on industrial development. The term 'industry' is somewhat vague though it is often used as synonymous with manufacturing. It is useful, however, because it is comprehensive. When dealing with, say, the chemical industry, one thinks of works and processes, but there are many activities which are not carried on in factories, such as what is now called the 'tourist industry' which certainly is an industry and an important one. There are times when for clarity one should use the long and ugly expression: 'manufacturing industry'. It prevents misunderstanding.

Let us then note that manufacture may be conducted in factories with modern power and mechanical equipment, or it may be still very primitive. There is a danger that we may forget the latter. Most of Asia and Africa still manufacture in the literal sense of the word. Japan in very modern. China has made little progress outside what used to be the "Treaty Ports"; even India is modern only in a few of the larger towns, and that for certain industries. Eastern Europe has little to show of modern factory development, except here and there. It is difficult to present a picture of these countries so that we tend to neglect them and turn our attention to the highly developed nations.

When approaching the subject of industrialisation and manufacture, an analysis of industrial occupations is the first thing to look at, but unhappily is not always available. Most countries, however, supply tables of various kinds so that one can soon get an idea of how things stand. Let us take a few examples, beginning with the U.S., because of its size and importance. The "Statistical Abstract of the U.S." will supply all the tables you wish and perhaps more. First you are told what is meant by a factory—"The quinquennial censuses . . . covered all factories or plants whose products were valued at $500 or more, but beginning with 1921, the minimum limit has been $5,000. Conceptually an establishment is a geographically isolated manufacturing unit maintaining independent book-keeping records regardless of its managerial or financial affiliations." That may or may not be clear, though one thinks a lawyer could enjoy himself discussing such a definition; nevertheless with the tables one can get along.

There were in 1939, unhappily the last available figures, 184,230 establishments employing 7,886,567 wage earners. The reader will be astonished at this figure, which is a good example of how careful we must be in looking at statistics. One needs to look back to the chapter headed 'Labor Force'. There, total occupations are given under two headings: (1) Experienced Labor Force; (2) Employed (except on public emergency work). There is a note explaining what these two terms mean, but it is far from clear exactly what is meant. It is a good example of the necessity for clear definition. As a lucky dip we will take (2). Here the total employed for the whole U.S. is 45,166,080. This figure is then broken up into major groups with sub-headings. One such group is craftsmen, foremen and kindred workers: 5,055,722, which would help to fill out our first low figure, but a good deal more investigation would be necessary.

Compare this 7,886,567 with the first returns for 1849 when there were 123,025 establishments with 957,059 wage earners

and one sees how the average size has increased. Another table
shows how the production per wage earner has increased. 1899
is taken as the base year. The increase is just double, a fact
which is worth careful consideration as it rather tempers the
belief in miracles. Two further tables are of great interest:

(1) MANUFACTURING ESTABLISHMENTS CLASSIFIED ACCORDING TO NUMBER OF WAGE-EARNERS ONLY FOR 1939

Table : Stat. Abs. for U.S.A. page 815.

Number of Wage Earners	Establish-ments	Average number of Wage Earners	Per cent of total	
			Establish-ments	Wage Earners
Total	184,230	7,886,567	100·0	100·0
None	8,315	—	4·5	—
1 to 5	75,930	203,052	41·2	2·6
6 to 20	49,015	542,679	26·6	6·9
21 to 50	23,646	764,814	12·8	9·7
51 to 100	11,908	848,423	6·5	10·8
101 to 250	9,458	1,472,651	5·1	18·7
251 to 500	3,653	1,268,983	2·0	16·1
501 to 1,000	1,495	1,024,297	·8	13·0
1,001 to 2,500	634	937,136	·3	11·9
2,501 or more	176	824,532	·1	10·5

Note that 85·1% of all the establishments employed 50 workers
or under who comprised 19·2% of the total workers; that 11·6%
employed between 51 and 250 workers, who comprised 29·5% of
the total workers, and that 3·2% employed between 251 and
2,501 +workers who comprised 51% of the total workers. It is
the usual picture and warns us against loose talk. The second
table is equally illuminating, 82·9% of all the establishments
employing 21·2% of the wage earners made 13·7% of the value
of all goods produced; 11·8% of the establishments employing
23·87% of the wage earners produced 18·9% of the total value,
while 5·27% of the establishments employing 52% of the
workers, produced 67·5% of the total value.

(2) MANUFACTURING ESTABLISHMENTS CLASSIFIED BY VALUE OF PRODUCTS 1939.

Table: Stat. Abs. for U.S.A. page 815.

Class of establishments according to value of products	Establishments		Wage Earners		Value of Products	
	Number	Per cent distribution	Average number	Per cent distribution	Amount (thousands of dollars)	Per cent distribution
Total	184,230	100·0	7,886,567	100·0	56,843,025	100·0
$5,000 to $19,999	60,593	32·9	189,575	2·4	680,777	1·2
$20,000 to $49,999	42,083	22·8	327,340	4·2	1,353,676	2·4
$50,000 to $99,999	25,490	13·8	389,637	4·9	1,811,463	3·2
$100,000 to $249,999	24,718	13·4	768,358	9·7	3,920,974	6·9
$250,000 to $499,999	13,066	7·1	839,222	10·6	4,626,937	8·1
$500,000 to $999,999	8,706	4·7	1,038,151	13·2	6,110,939	10·8
$1,000,000 to $2,499,999	6,088	3·3	1,463,278	18·6	9,298,230	16·4
$2,500,000 to $4,999,999	2,013	1·1	904,184	11·5	6,918,927	12·2
$5,000,000 and over	1,473	·8	1,966,822	24·9	22,121,102	38·9

These two tables show a rough coincidence, but what we want to notice is that big industry does play a dominant part in the life of the U.S. Two-thirds of the manufacturing values of this vast country come from 5% of the factories. If we made further inquiries we should find that many of these great establishments belong to some great combine or trust.

One more table may be mentioned—that giving more or less the same detail as above, but for individual regions and states. There are three outstanding groups: (1) The New England States, particularly Massachusetts, Rhode Island and Connecticut: (2) The Middle Atlantic with the three States of New York, New Jersey and Pennsylvania: (3) The East North Central, comprising Ohio, Indiana, Illinois, Michigan and Wisconsin, though the last is not outstanding. These three groups together account for 5,399,000 wage earners out of roughly 7,887,000.

Now let us turn in contrast to India,[1] which has nearly three times the U.S. population. The tables are not nearly so full or

[1] Before partition.

so numerous, so that our comparison must be very rough.
The difficulty is to get up-to-date and accurate figures. A. R.
Prest in his recent book, *War Economics of Primary Producing
Countries*, writes: "Any attempt to estimate the overall changes
in the Indian manufacturing position during the war years would
be extremely hazardous, in view of the scarcity of available
statistics on the subject." I shall quote from the "Statistical
Abstract for 1943," and from Prest: the analysis by occupation
gives 17,524,000 in industry, which is not, at first sight, vastly
different from the U.S., though it is a smaller proportion. It
makes 10·38% of the occupied population. Other interesting
figures are 65·6% for agriculture and ·24% for mining. Such a
number employed in industry, if working in modern factories,
would mean a large output and would enable the standard of
living to be different from that which prevails. When, however,
we look at the statistics given under the heading of 'Industries'
we find a different story. There were only 2,037,000 wage earners
working in modern factories in 1938. Of factories of any kind
there were 11,460, but many of these were only workshops.
There was a very slow expansion going on though five years of
war slightly accelerated it, as will be seen from the table which
I have taken from Prest.

BRITISH INDIA—VOLUME OF FACTORY EMPLOYMENT (000's)

Industry	1939	1944
Total No. employed	1751	2517
(a) Government and local fund factories	132	419
(b) All other factories	1619	2098
(i) Textiles	817	993
(ii) Engineering	148	265
(iii) Minerals and Metals	55	94
(iv) Food, drink, tobacco	247	294
(v) Chemicals, dyes	58	90
(vi) Paper and Printing	44	53
(vii) Wood, stone, glass	52	96
(viii) Hides, skins	13	35
(ix) Gins and presses	163	143
(x) Miscellaneous	22	35

This expansion however is merely based upon the number of work people on the pay rolls. How effective they were can be seen from the next table.

INDUSTRIAL PRODUCTION

Commodity	1939	1944
Coal (m. tons)	—	26·5
Paper (ooo's cwt.)	1416	2001
Pig iron (ooo's tons)	—	1303
Steel ingots (ooo's tons)	—	1264
Cement (ooo's tons)	—	2044
Sugar (ooo's tons)	1241	985
Jute manufactures (ooo's tons)	1277	975
Cotton piecegoods (m. yd.)	4012	4695
Cotton yarn (m. lb.)	1243	1620
Footwear (m. pairs)	—	6·0
Sulphuric acid (ooo's cwt.)	—	778

Source. "Monthly Survey Business Conditions," (and miscellaneous others); "Recent Social and Economic Trends in India."

Notes. (1) Figures are for all India.
(2) Figures for jute manufactures include twist and yarn.
(3) Figures for sugar refer to factory-refined white sugar only.

The reasons for this lack of result are: (1) that modern industry requires modern machinery which is all imported into India. Machine making can be said to have hardly begun; (2) the Indian workers drawn in from the villages are wholly unskilled; (3) India still lacks an adequate 'foreman' class.

The industries which stand out in India are the two textiles, cotton and jute, which account for a high proportion of the factory population—some 811,000. The engineering industries expanded from 143,000 in 1938 to 265,000 in 1944, but this figure can be checked by the volume of output, which was small.

Here, then, is a complete contrast with the U.S. India may be said to be just beginning as a modern industrialised country. Contrast the background against which this manufacturing industry takes place in the two countries, and it gives food for thought. Both the Indian Dominions are ambitious and wish to develop modern industries on a large scale, as indeed they must if the standards of living are to be raised. Already we have before us the Bombay Plan, which can be obtained in a Penguin. The late British Government in India was more cautious in its planning and less ambitious in its targets. Here the geographer can have much to say, and if one may say so here, enthusiasm does seem to qualify sound thinking.

The distribution of these modern factories is given by provinces. Three provinces stand out: Bombay, Bengal and Madras. This is interesting as they are the three old Presidencies and have been longest under European influence; also education is more advanced. Two other provinces—the U.P. and the Punjab make up the rest for all intents and purposes, but they are far behind the first three. Further examination shows how these factories cluster primarily round the great ports and a few large inland towns, such as Cawnpore and Lahore, but except perhaps for, say, three or four centres, one would not consider them heavily industrialised.

As a third example let us glance at the United Kingdom. It contrasts in every way with the two examples already given. In size 94,200 sq. miles, compared with the U.S. 3,033,000, not including Alaska, and India's 1,675,000; in population roughly 50,000,000 as compared with 141,000,000 and 400,000,000 respectively. All sorts of comparisons and contrasts can be made, but one must be careful. The first obvious fact is the difference in size—94,000 sq. miles, which is a limited area within which to operate, even when it is all available. The second thing is the high density of population and the very high degree of urbanisation, which must mean manufactures and commerce. There is then the lack of minerals, except coal and some iron, and the lack of raw materials in general. Contrast with the U.S. and then contrast the U.S. with India, which is only very moderately endowed. The *Annual Abstract of*

Statistics[1] has much to tell us. In Section VII, 'Production', the
first table gives us the production in the principal industrial areas.
Unfortunately the figures stop at 1935, but this discussion is
more for instruction than information as such, so it will not
matter too much.   The trends have not altered very much, so
the table is still useful.

1935	Establish- ments	Average No. employed	Net output per person
United Kingdom	64,696	7,305,500	222
England & Wales	56,931	6,494,500	225
Scotland	6,525	670,800	213
Northern Ireland	1,240	140,200	143
Greater London	15,171	1,467,000	272
Lancs, Cheshire & the Glossop & New Mills of Derbyshire	9,772	1,232,900	202
West Riding of Yorkshire	6,644	799,100	200
Warwickshire, Worcester- shire & Staffordshire	6,702	891,400	221

Notice the number of establishments—64,696, and compare them
with the U.S.—184,230.   That seems to be about the right
proportion.   It is somewhat higher than the U.S. and might be
due either to our greater urbanisation, or to the average size
being slightly greater in the U.S., but you need to be careful.
Then compare the figures for the wage earners and they are
roughly the same size, which seems very curious, as indeed it is.
The fact is the figures and tables are not comparable.   The U.S.
figures are rigidly limited to factory workers, while ours include
non-factory workers, such as building and contracting, mines and
quarries, publicity services and government departments, which
together account for 2,147,900.   Even when this correction is
made, one does not feel satisfied, and indeed the occupational
heading in the U.S. analysis "Craftsmen, foremen and kindred
workers"—which totals just under 6,000,000, would help to solve
the problem.   It would be a very difficult matter to make
comparison.

[1] 1935–46.

.Let us return to the table. The thing which strikes one at once is the predominance of England. This is brought out again when one looks at the population figures. Out of a total estimated population of just over 49,000,000, roughly 41,000,000 live and work in England. It can be seen from all the production figures. One should remember, too, that the area of England alone is just over 50,000 sq. miles. It is then that one sees the very great congestion. The table gives all the principal industrial areas and I have chosen four. These 'areas' are very arbitrary affairs and were not made by geographers, but even had they been, they would still have been arbitrary. The importance of Greater London stands out, while the number of persons per establishment is less, as we would expect. The output per worker is higher. Notice the importance of the Lancashire, Cheshire area, which comes next, and also remark the lower production per worker as compared with both the United Kingdom and Greater London.

There is a corresponding table to that of the U.S., giving size and number of establishments and the numbers employed. The numbers do not agree with those in the first table, and are again due to definition. Thus the first table includes non-factory trades. It does not matter for our present purpose, which is to show how varied is the size of the factories.

SIZE OF ESTABLISHMENTS IN FACTORY TRADES, 1935

	Establishments	Employed	Net output per person
All establishments	181,282	5,694,200	
10 and under	132,338	536,600	
11–24	16,490	279,200	212
25–49	12,542	437,500	214
50–99	8,582	601,600	217
100–199	5,754	804,800	214
200–299	2,248	547,600	215
300–399	1,146	394,200	213
400–499	602	267,900	205
500–749	716	434,700	233
750–999	331 ⎫	284,200	232
1,000–1,499	267 ⎬ 30%	323,700	241
1,500 & over	266 ⎭	782,200	286

It is interesting to notice that while the per capita output goes up with the larger establishments, it is not as much as one would expect, nor so marked as in the U.S. Establishments of 750 upwards accounted for 30% of the gross output and employed 27% of the wage earner.

Let us now consider what these superficial comparisons have done for us. First, they have shown how very difficult comparison is. The appeal to statistics seems so scientific and final, but we find that the statistics do not allow of easy comparison. It would be necessary to go much more fully into the figures before we could quote them as authoritative. This is the common error which may be made in innocence or wickedness. Statistics do not lie when properly handled, but few people are capable of doing it. Second, words are so misleading; a workman may mean anyone from a highly skilled, alert and hard-working man, to something which is so-called because it is a male found on a factory premises, and the higher authorities insist that it shall be so-called. We need to know the quality of the labour, whether it be that of a miner, a doctor, or whatever you will. We need qualitative statistics.

What we have found out by means of these scanty figures does help us, though we should require a more detailed study before we could begin to feel sure of ourselves. It makes a beginning, but one thing we cannot get out of books and that is that clothing of the dry bones of statistics with living flesh, unless we know the places and peoples at first hand, and then intimately. There must be personal knowledge. Professor F. M. Powicke, in his recently published *Three Lectures*, speaks of the use of statistics to the historian, but adds a warning: "Here the historical imagination can come into its own, to check the dangers latent in the statistical method." The historian cannot go back to the Middle Ages; there is no 'time-machine' except imagination based upon facts. We geographers can travel, at least some of us can sometimes, but we can use that highly trained imagination to which Professor Powicke alludes. Even the most highly trained statistician, using his figures with all his skill, can be desperately wrong if he lacks personal knowledge and sympathetic imagination. That is where so much of the modern planning goes wrong.

Each country needs to be studied in this way, which means that the magnitude of the task is beyond any one man. At some point we must begin to specialise, even though that specialisation be not taken far. It will follow as a matter of course that in these studies some routine of approach will be adopted partly from habit, but partly because it helps to 'tidy' up a somewhat disorderly world. One would not be scientific if one were not orderly and tidy, but one needs to be on one's guard. It is not only the middle class who suffer from being suburbia-minded. Professor Powicke, in the same lectures, quotes Dr. Inge as saying "Historians are born snobs," and expands the statement: "like all snobs, historians tend to bow down before accepted facts." He goes on to say: "Philosophers have said a good deal on their behalf. No true poet does this kind of thing." So with us economic geographers, we all tend to be snobs, worshipping the accepted facts as standardised in each of our own countries. The Englishman knows the world he wants to create; so does the American and the Russian, and the approach to the facts is via their respective suburbias. It is well to be aware of this bias, so that we can use the routines with discrimination, and so that the poet can illuminate both our minds and our task.

For instance, in our own case, we tend to direct our study too much to international trade. The reasons are fairly obvious and indeed it would not be possible to study the economic geography of the British Isles without being aware of them, but even with our own country we can overdo the emphasis, or shall we say under-emphasise the total economic background? This attitude has certainly been one of the factors retarding our efforts in the development of the colonial empire in the past. Many of our worst failures in India arose out of this accepted belief that as we had developed so it must be good for India. In this we are not alone; it is so with others. Most people tend to approach the study of manufacture through the iron and steel industries, the heavy engineering trades, chemical industries, heavy and light; the automobile industry, the textiles and in our own case at least, shipbuilding. There is no harm in so doing provided one does not think that industrialisation implies all, or most of these. This pattern of thinking has become of more importance since the Russian industrial revolution and with the growing realisation that 'plans' can be imposed upon backward, as well as relatively up-to-date, countries. Such plans have been, and are being suggested for the industrialisation of Eastern and South Eastern Europe—for India and China, to take the better known cases. In the Victorian free-trade England it was rather assumed that industrialisation would take place 'naturally' when the country was ripe for development. This belief was not subscribed to elsewhere, and Frederich List's *National System of Political Economy* is the classical denial of this belief, but List did not visualise a 'planned economy' as understood today.

That a planned economy can be imposed successfully has been demonstrated by Russia, but that a similar imposing of some such plan would be successful elsewhere does not necessarily follow, especially in densely populated and only moderately endowed countries, such as India and China, nor can one affect to ignore the human price demanded, but this denial does not rule out alternatives where the planning is of a less intensive and absolute order. The alternatives are posed by P. N. Rosenstein-Roden in an article in the *Economic Journal*, No 210–211 of 1943, where he suggests an alternative to the Russian model. No doubt by this time the Russians themselves have also 'suggested' modifications to the model. The possible plans then are: (1) The Russian model, which could only be applied in its purity to large units such as India, China or South-Eastern Europe. (2) Some less intensive plan as suggested by Rosenstein-Roden, which would fit the individual countries into the world economy. (3) A still less planned development rather on the lines laid down by List and assisted, to some extent, by foreign loans, foreign advice and foreign technicians. (4) The Victorian *laissez-faire*.

Except for communists and die-hard free traders, the first and fourth are ruled out. The middle two tend to merge into one another and present possibilities which are well developed in

Rodenstein-Roden's article.   It does not inevitably follow that this planning need be governmental, and the reader's attention is directed to the International Basic Economy Corporation (IBEC) which has been set up by Mr. Rockefeller for development in South America.   Already it has begun operations in Venezuela and Brazil.   People with pink complexions may go slightly pinker at such a plan but I suggest that the economic geographer, being a scientist, first examines the plan before passing sentence.   When finally considering the matter of planning, it might be well to read Professor Jewkes' *Trial by Planning*.   This is a book which demands serious consideration.

How one plans will, of course, depend a good deal upon one's hopes and fears.   Autarky is the child of fear.   The fear that war will find one without all that is necessary to wage it with. The Germans never forgot our blockade in the first war.   Fear, as a neutral, that one will go short of certain commodities, but this is a lesser fear; fear of the trade-cycle upsetting the domestic peace; fear that one's ideology will be contaminated.   Fear, like hate, is a negative thing and no real civilisation can be based upon them.   One should notice how the fear of war casts its shadow upon us all.   The younger generation never having known a world without fear will hardly realise what a good life can be like unless they have internal peace.   Given a world such as ours today, the iron and steel and heavy engineering trades, as well as the chemical, become vitally necessary.   In a world set free, one could, and did, take a different view.   Industrialisation might be contemplated without these heavy industries. Let us consider the future development, of say, New Zealand, which had in 1944 a population of 1,676,000.   The total area is 103,000 sq. miles, which is somewhat larger than the United Kindgom.   South Island is almost exactly the same area as England and Wales.   Suppose the population has reached 10,000,000, how do you think it will be occupied?   A somewhat foolish question, but good exercise.   No doubt a pastoral agriculture would not suffice and some considerable degree of industrialisation would take place.   The 'normal' routine used to be that one began with the textile industries.   New Zealand has one textile at hand, wool, and the import of cotton is not impossible. Would the heavy industries be necessary? No, though no doubt efforts would be made to develop them. Plans were laid for starting an iron and steel industry, but may be that was because we humans are all snobs, as above defined. A certain French Premier of some long time ago, justified his tariff increases by saying he liked to see the factory chimneys smoke. There is more in that cryptic remark than first appears, and it may provide a possible clue to the New Zealand desire for an iron and steel industry. All this, of course, applies only to a world set free, otherwise, a little steel may be better than no steel. New Zealand in a decent world, might develop into a considerably industrialised state, with such industries as certain textiles, light engineering and light chemical, leaving many of the heavy industries and the automobile industries to others.

Before closing this chapter one might comment upon some of the quick ways of appraising a country's industrial development. These are useful if used with care and discretion. Coal consumption used to be a common way of judging a country's industrial position. This is not the same as coal production. Thus we today consume more coal in industry than we did pre-war, though we produce less. The explanation, is of course, that we have ceased almost to export, and domestic consumption has been curtailed, but coal consumption in industry may not be the only indication of power used. We must ascertain how much oil and hydro-electricity is used, and this may be very considerable in some countries. Electricity with us is practically all coal-generated and must not be double counted. When making comparisons with the past, allowance must be made for more efficient burning of coal and more efficient power transmission systems. One should remember it when comparing different countries. If, for instance, you look up the coal burnt in India, plus the hydro-electricity and oil employed, one has a shrewd idea of how India stands. This applies to all countries. Efficiency, too, can often be guessed by the proportion of electrical drive to steam, but again one must be cautious. Another measure is the tonnage output of iron and steel. At one time

the pig iron tonnage was a most useful lowest common denomi-
nator in the iron and steel, and the engineering industries, but is
no longer so, as so much steel is made from scrap.   It is better
to take the steel tonnages, but lowest common denominators
have their limitations.   Steel is not a simple homogeneous thing
like pure gold is, it may be a hundred and one different kinds.
For this country the British Iron and Steel Federation issue
annual statistics where we can see in some detail what they are
making.   Never quote the number of blast furnaces, as they
can be of very varying tonnage capacity.

For the textile industries the number of spindles is useful
on the spinning side, and looms on the weaving, but they do not
tell us much.   One needs to know the number of revolutions
and the number of picks per minute.   In addition, one needs to
know how many are operating, and for how many hours a week.
Idle machinery doesn't produce much.   On the whole it is better
to take the output of yarn and to take it in its classification of
counts.   Cotton cloth yardage doesn't tell one a great deal at
first sight as cloth is too vague a term;   it can mean anything
from the cheapest dhotis to the most expensive muslins;   it may
be unbleached, bleached, coloured.   Here there is no simple
index.   In the past it was useful to note how many of the spindles
were ring, and how many mule;   ring spinning used to imply
coarse and low medium counts, while mule spinning implied
the higher counts.   The gap has been narrowed of late years,
so that one must be more cautious.

These things help, but like most short-hand methods, they
are dangerous when employed by those who do not know their
limitations;   in any case they do not go far.   Finally, in judging
industrial power one must look at outputs which are the summation of all the efforts.   Often these outputs are added together
in values, so that one gets a money figure.   In the *Annual
Abstract of Statistics*, there is a table giving 'Production by
principal industrial groups.'   Here is summarised the money
value of the principal industries.   The figures are given in gross
and net.   It helps us to see quickly the comparative importance of
the various industries.   Thus the total net value of all trades in
1935 was £1625·1 million.   The Iron and Steel Industry contri-

buted £116·5 million; textiles, £157·5 million: chemicals £201·5 million. Money values change so one must make allowance for such changes. When one needs fuller information one is driven to the enormous lists which name each article produced. Both approaches are necessary.

CHAPTER VII

GOVERNMENTAL POLICIES AND INTERFERENCE

THE smaller economic geographies, and often the longer ones, present their facts without any reference to the environments in which men work and live. The environment is either taken for granted or ignored. This is a serious mistake even in the case of one's own country for which one has a certain feeling but it is a grave matter when dealing with the outside world. We have seen already how much it matters that the cultural background should constantly be remembered and how important are standards of living. The cultural background with its related standards can make itself felt in the economic world in two ways: through customary relationships where the society is relatively static: through governmental action of different kinds in modern societies. Both ways will be found influencing the environments in which men live and work though the latter has become the major factor in modern communities. The customary relationships have been glanced at and now we must turn to the more conscious and direct interference by government action.

There never was a time when government did not interfere in some way in the economic life of those governed, but this interference was partial or fitful largely owing to lack of techniques of control. The totalitarian state is not a new phenomenon, but only a throw back, at least in Western Europe, to the old idea of how a state should be run. Much of the religious persecution of the past was due to the belief that the state had the right to regulate religious belief which was considered vital to right thinking and right living. In our own country, state interference in economic life has grown steadily since Elizabethan times. If today we are planning as never before, it is due to the development of scientific thought and its application to everyday life. We are all planners, that is the joke of it. It is only the other man's plan to which we object. No one really believes in *laissez-faire*, not even the business man who when really left to himself immediately begins to plan combines and monopolies just as the workman forms a trade union. The real problem is to maintain a just balance between control and liberty of action and that will depend (1) upon the degree of accurate knowledge we possess; (2) upon the techniques of control which will be devised, (3) the human ability to manipulate these controls honestly and wisely, and (4) the belief of those controlled and interfered with that the control is necessary and serves a purpose. All these things will vary from time to time. Thus in war one puts up with an infinite regulation of one's life even as a civilian: still more so as a member of the forces.

Governmental action may aim primarily at control of the internal development of a country or of the foreign trade, but whichever method is employed it must affect both as both form part of the whole pattern. Thus a communist state, to take the extreme example of control, plans and controls the whole economic life of the state: it must therefore control equally closely all foreign trade. The approach is primarily through the internal activities but the external ones are automatically affected. The opposite case would be a country such as the U.S. today or ourselves between the two wars. Here there is little direct attempt to control internal activities and development which are left largely to themselves, though there were the beginnings of direct interference in our case, but by means of such things as tariffs and exchange control, the external activities are consciously affected. Again, however, the reaction is at once evident. Protection or free trade must affect industrial activity internally. We see therefore that any division between methods is more one of intention than results in operation. The more drastic the action taken either way, the more complete the total controls. Thus to repeat the case of communist Russia. Complete internal control implies complete external. A communist state could not be a free trade state. Again a state which imposed protective duties which were prohibitively high could kill all foreign trade but by doing so would fundamentally alter its internal pattern of industry even though there were no direct interference in home industries. It is where the controls are only partial and light that the primary intent is evident. Even then it would be wrong to imagine that their effects ceased at that point. It should be noticed that controls which are intended to have positive effects in the country imposing them must have negative ones upon those other countries with which trade is being conducted. Thus if, as used to be the case long ago, South Wales exports large amounts of tin-plate to the U.S. and that country in order to develop its own tin-plate industry enforces a heavy tariff, the negative effect upon South Wales can be very grave. In pre-1914 days these negative effects though obvious—Macgregor in his brilliant analysis *Industrial Combination* brings it out—were not of the magnitude that they became in the 'thirties' when the trading countries succeeded in almost strangling each other. It is the memory of those unhappy and unprofitable days which led to Bretton Woods and all the more recent attempts to achieve common action in international trading affairs.

State policies attempting, whether positively or negatively, to regulate and control economic industries are themselves the outcome of the environment which they attempt to regulate though they may be the result of doctrinaire thinking based upon a simplification which is carried so far as to make the relationship not easily apparent. Communism is one answer to a complex economic and social world: socialism another: *laissez-faire* and capitalism with or without the moderating influence of social legislation such as that of our own country: the New Deal in the U.S., all are policies which attempt each in its own way to bring order and justice into a world which grows increasingly complex. One needs to study these recently past environments to see how they have influenced thought and action but such a study would take up too much space. The next few paragraphs, which break away from the main theme, must be read as pointers showing the way to study and approach this recent past in which will be found as ever the economic and spiritual all mixed together. One then picks up the thread of the argument.

The attempt at internal control may be complete and systematic as in the case of countries under communist or socialist control or it may be partial and haphazard as in countries which are not. The former type are theoretically more logical and have a definite appeal to all scientific and logical folk. They need to be studied with care. As economic geographers we want and need to know all we can about the U.S.S.R. The fact we know so little is to be deplored. Even if one totally disagrees with communism it does not alter the fact that a large portion of the earth's surface is controlled by a government professing communism. The effects of this control for good or evil are there. Of course at this point Mr. Bernard Shaw would insist upon producing his dictionary and making us look up the meaning of communism and whatever it was either Mr. Molotov or the Dean of Canterbury would say no. We must, therefore, if we are to study the economic geography of the U.S.S.R., know as far as we can how that State is organised and how the machine works. Unhappily it is impossible to get a detached view. All the literature on Russia is heavily biased and is bound to be where such strong emotional appeals are made.

The U.S. might be taken as the type of *laissez-faire* capitalist country. Not that there is not a great mass of industrial legislation and anti-trust laws. Americans would, however, say that with the exception of the New Deal legislation these were merely the rules of the ring made to see that the fight within the ropes was a fair one. The same would be true of our own country, certainly till 1914, and probably much later. Whether a Russian would agree or whether those passengers travelling by the same train in an easterly direction would agree is another matter. What is a fair fight? It would seem to depend upon how desperate is the fight and what are the rules. Is all-in wrestling fair fighting? But to return. Here within the ropes 'capital' has organised itself in varying ways from the simple small capitalist running a small works or farm or shop to the great combines by whatsoever name known; trust, syndicate, or cartel. All these forms of organisation should be understood. There are several small books dealing with these: Robertson, *Control of Industry*, is a good beginning. 'Labour' has organised itself in the great Trade Unions. These too must be understood both in themselves and in their relationships with the 'capitalist' organisations such as the Federation of British Industries and with the State. Who rule the country today? The Cabinet, the T.U.C. or the shop stewards? It is important to know.

Great Britain today is a semi-socialist state. One cannot say it is "completely and systematically" organised as is Russia, nor can one allege that like the U.S. or ourselves prior to 1938 the laws are merely to keep the ring clear. When the Iron and Steel Industry has been nationalised the Government will however have control of all the major levers: quite apart from the other pressures which can be directly and indirectly applied.

For a proper understanding of the world today it is necessary to study with some care the inter-war period. It does not make pleasant reading but it is certainly interesting for in those years developed the movements which have been and are so profoundly affecting us. The most concise study on the economic side is Arndt's *Economic Lessons of the Nineteen Thirties*, issued from the "Royal Institute of International Affairs". This is no easy reading as it is very condensed in spite of its 300 pages. It deals with highly controversial matter and so exhibits a 'bias' as must all such books. The reader might well begin by reading the Appendix which is a dissenting note by Sir Andrew McFadyean and Professor A. G. B. Fisher. Not that the reader need or will agree with these gentlemen who might be described as Liberals. The author rather shares their views with qualifications. The criticism is more or less summed up in the second paragraph: "I believe that the general impression which would be left on the mind of any reader of this study not equipped by experience for its critical examination would be that, to use Bradley's famous definition of optimism, the world between 1919 and 1939 'was the best of all possible worlds and everything in it was a necessary evil.'" The reader is strongly recommended to read the first chapter which is a kind of précis of the rest; then if he feels inclined he can read the special chapters which elaborate this. After that he can read the last chapter entitled 'The Lessons,' which deal with unemployment and various international problems. Another book is *British Economic Foreign Policy* by J. H. Richardson, written some few years before Arndt's and dealing only with ourselves. There are very useful chapters on Commercial Policy, Imperial Trade Policy and Agricultural Policy. It is not nearly so condensed as Arndt's.

What was happening in these years and were all those in authority foolish or even worse? Most readers will come to these problems with their minds already made up so that they will be impatient at points of view which differ from their own. There are so many facts that it is possible almost innocently to pick those which suit one's own case. It is practically impossible to be objective beyond a point. Facts there are which cannot be disputed. All these facts will be found in these two books. How we interpret the facts will depend upon one's beliefs which are certainly not objective. Is it wrong to have two wives? In this country, yes. When pressed to say why, many will reply because it is unchristian. Whether they are objectively right is not quite easy to say. St. Paul merely laid down that a bishop must not have more than one. The implication is that some Christians had more, but present day interpretation definitely says one. In a Mohammedan country, however, two wives would be permitted both by the law and moral code. Incidentally a plurality of wives is exceedingly rare in Mohammedan countries. Common ideas of the East are still largely based upon the *Arabian Nights*, which nevertheless are eminently worth reading, and such plays as *Alf's Button* which while being popular is hardly veracious.

Points of view as to what constitutes social justice will largely determine how the reader will interpret the facts in Arndt's book but the facts are there and correctly stated. The reader can then interpret. Now there has been a vast amount of thinking about and criticism of the social system in this and other countries during the past hundred years. This has coincided with and been intimately related with the development of science which has challenged most of the social and religious dogmas. That, however, is not all. A great deal of the challenge and the criticism has come from another source, the Christian religion. You don't need to be a 'scientist' to want social justice: you only need to be a Christian. The scandals and horrors of the industrial revolution do not expose the failure of the Christian ethic but of those who failed to apply it. Science and religion

E

may have fought each other but that was merely because of the arrogance and stupid pride based upon ignorance of the combatants. True science and true religion cannot be antagonistic as both search for the truth. There is tragedy and comedy in the great controversy between the exponents of Darwinian evolution and those ardent fundamentalists who opposed it in the name of religion. The churchmen were right though they were wrong, and the Darwinians were wrong though they were right. No evolutionist today accepts the Darwinian explanation. What both scientists and Christians greatly need is humility. God is not a fly to be encased in the petrified gum of human knowledge or experience. While this great ferment in ideas has been going on the techniques of production have been revolutionising industry. The flow of goods has steadily increased bringing with it new problems of distribution. Again one comes back to the patterns of industry and living; not two patterns so much as the same pattern looked at in reverse. Industry exists for the sake of production and production is for consumption. The two must coincide, for if they do not there will be trouble. If we go back to, say, the post-Waterloo period, most of what we would call the extreme austerity of those times was due to the fact that practically all production was still by hand. Even where machinery was employed it was exceedingly crude and inefficient. One could have said to the mass of the people: you can't have much more simply because it does not exist. Poverty and scarcity were understandable. In the great world depression of 1929–34 such a plea could not be put forward. The world had to witness the tragic sight of starvation and want in the midst of potential plenty. The new techniques of production were there, the raw material was so plentiful it had to be destroyed, labour wanted work as well as goods. Here was something new. Not new in the sense that there had not been trade cycles before with their booms and depressions but new in the magnitude of the breakdown. It is foolish to put the blame for this at the door of any one set of men. The explanation fundamentally lay in the fact that twentieth century production had not been geared in with a twentieth century distribution. Mass production must imply mass consumption otherwise the belts must stop. The distributive system was still 19th century. Now systems of distribution imply more than economics: morals and ethics come into them. Economics mostly operates within postulated points and so is largely conditional. Somewhere Alfred Marshall remarked that when visiting factories he could nearly always price accurately an operative's work. There was an implication that this was due to the fact that he was an economist which was true only to a limited sense. The combination of new techniques in production with the ethical challenge 'is it just', 'is it fair', have made men challenge these postulates. Life becomes difficult when social postulates are universally challenged, and impossible when the axioms are denied, for not all the limiting points in economics or the social sciences are postulates. Sometimes it is difficult to distinguish which is which.

In the attempt to bring order out of chaos new and social economic theories have been evolved and put into practice: Communism in Russia and Eastern Europe: Nazism and Fascism in Germany and Italy, the New Deal in the U.S., while in the U.K. socialism crept in the Fabian way until with the recent elections it has come by direct policy. All these are or were, with qualifications, intended to reconstruct or modify the internal economic and social structure. All are attempts to solve the same economic and social problems, the great and difficult problem of distribution and the equally difficult one of social equality. A very useful introduction to all this will be found in *Economic Problems of Today* by W. Arthur Lewis. Part I deals with 'The Nature of the Problems', and Part II 'The Solutions Adopted Abroad'. An excellent introduction for the beginner and well worth reading by others. It is, however, well to remember that we humans seldom like the pure milk of the word. We soon introduce a dash of something stronger, which particular spirit depending upon the national temperament and background. This is so in religion. What exactly is the essence of the Christian faith? Whatever it is, each age, each people, will approach it from their own particular angle. Hence the variety of Christians, a fact which often calls for caustic remark but which shows how little the critic understands Christianity.

Buddhism is also interesting. Here is a 'religion' which denies the existence of God and so it is atheistical, but as time has gone on Buddhists being human have elevated the Buddha himself to that lofty position. In Tibet, Buddhism has combined with devil worship to produce that very interesting form of Lamaism, but Buddha would be greatly surprised if he could visit Tibet. So again the Buddhists of Japan have modified their practice. This difference between theory and practice is important when examining the various types of national approach to their economic problems. So with the new social systems we are about to discuss. There is a vast difference between the communism of Professor Laski's little book and that of Imperial Russia today. Socialism may mean many things and he would be a clever man who could divide left wing socialism from communism and the ultra liberalised capitalism of this country from the right. What the New Deal really was and aimed at let the reader ask the Americans.

We now return to our main discussion and will illustrate what we have been saying by a brief consideration of Great Britain's trade policies between the wars and then by some discussion of the full employment policy and its implications.

Between 1860 and 1914 Great Britain had been a free trade country, during which time its trade and industry had vastly expanded as indeed had that of the whole world. Population had also greatly increased and with it urbanisation while standards of living had greatly advanced. One industry only had failed to expand and indeed had barely held its own, agriculture. More and more the country had come to depend upon overseas supplies, so that by the outbreak of war we were only 40% self supporting. This state of affairs had caused little alarm though Joseph Chamberlain had already tried to convert the nation to protection. The nation, however, did not agree with him as shown in the elections and their view seemed amply supported by the fact that right up to 1914 all industries showed increased outputs while foreign trade flourished in spite of German and other competition.

After the war things did not go so well. Foreign competition greatly increased: markets were lost and unemployment not only increased for a time but seemed permanent. Then came the great depression accentuating the unemployment and threatening even more severe competition. In 1932 protection was formally adopted when the Import Duties Act became operative. There had been some protection of key industries before this but in 1930 80% of the imports came in free. At the same time the Ottawa Agreements of 1932 attempted to divert trade from foreign countries to the Empire. Agriculture being one of the depressed industries was included in these schemes and it is with this which we shall deal by way of example.

The position was difficult. The country was importing roughly 60% of its foodstuffs and of these imports 58% came from foreign countries and the rest from the Empire. The shares for home, foreign and empire production were roughly 40%, 35%, and 25%, though the percentages of the various commodities produced and imported varied greatly. To the common sense man the objective seemed clear. Here was farming in a very bad way. There was no doubt about that. On the other hand imports of cereals, fruits, butter, bacon, beef and mutton were very heavy. Here are certain figures.

VALUE OF CERTAIN BRITISH FOOD IMPORTS IN 1931.[1]
(in £ million).

	Foreign	Empire
Bacon and hams	34·6	1·7
Chilled beef	20·1	—
Frozen beef	0·9	1·9
Frozen mutton and lamb	5·0	13·2
Butter and cheese	25·9	29·4
Wheat and wheated flour	18·0	16·4
Barley, oats and maize	14·6	1·4
Eggs	13·3	3·3
Apples	4·3	3·6
Other fresh fruit (incl. tomatoes)	5·5	2·2
Potatoes	5·9	1·0
Fresh vegetables	1·6	—

[1] Richardson: *British Economic Foreign Policy*.

What simpler than to encourage home supply by means of tariffs and other devices. Everyone knew that by raising home prices the British farmer would be able to compete and so the farming industry would be saved while the nation would be safer in case of war. Not that people were thinking seriously of war in 1932: nor were many remembering the effects of the German submarine campaign in the late war.

The problem was, however, much more complicated than it appeared. We can leave out for present purposes the intricate network of trade agreements which always exist between countries and which make negotiations a very tricky affair. Like Agag the negotiator has to walk delicately, weaving his way over and under sometimes hundreds of strands. Arm-chair negotiators forget this. There was the first fact that the U.K. was a great creditor nation and had to be paid. The Argentine Railways had been largely built by British capital and interest was expected. New Zealand, Australia, India, just to mention a few debtors, also expected and were expected to pay their debts. These payments are made nominally in terms of money but actually in commodities. A debtor can only pay his debt under two conditions: (1) that he has a surplus over and above what is necessary to live and (2) that the creditor will accept this surplus. This latter condition was not fully realised until German reparations made it painfully clear. New Zealand for instance as our debtor could only pay its debt if we accepted surplus produce of its mutton, wool, butter and cheese. So with Australia and the Argentine. If we did not take their produce they could not pay us. It was about this time when there was much talk of protecting our agriculture that the then Prime Minister of New Zealand said somewhere in a speech that if the English did not take their produce then they would not pay their debts. This was taken by some to be a threat to repudiate the New Zealand debts. Actually it was merely a statement of cause and effect. New Zealand exports were almost entirely pastoral products and 73% of the total exports in 1929 came to the U.K. This increased to 88·0% in 1932. If therefore we refused the New Zealand exports or reduced them considerably then it would be impossible for the debt transfer to be made. The proposal to protect British agriculture in view of these facts demanded careful thought. It involved other considerations too. If food exporting countries found the volume of their exports limited then their ability to buy from us would be affected. Clapping on a tariff is not so easy as it seems especially if there are alternative markets in which to buy. At the same time the Dominions were demanding an increased share in the U.K. food imports and if they were to be satisfied then countries like the Argentine and Denmark must have less. Apart from commercial considerations the proposals raise a moral one which was very strikingly brought out in the case of Denmark and our attempt to increase the supply of home-cured bacon. Between 1927–32 about 85% of the bacon consumed in this country was imported. Of the imports more than 90% were foreign and most of that Danish. The marketing scheme for pigs and bacon aimed at increasing considerably the home supply and at the same time giving an increased share of the import to Canada and New Zealand. Such a policy was bound to react very violently and unfavourably upon the Danes who for many decades had organised their industry especially for the British market on a tacit understanding that we should buy. Some of us are old enough to remember that Danish bacon like Danish butter was good. Suddenly these tacit understandings are swept away. The Danes perforce agreed 'voluntarily' to restrict their exports by 20%. When unexpectedly home supplies turned out to be more than was anticipated a further attempt was made by negotiation to reduce the import still further. Negotiations failed and a cut of 16% was imposed. In all this we had a perfect right, legally. No treaty was broken though the 16% cut was a violation of the quota principle enunciated by the British Government at the World Economic Conference in 1933. Again the Government was legally correct as the principle had not been embodied in any signed agreement. If one stands by strict business legality what we did was perfectly permissible. But was it moral? The Danes had always dealt with us in a scrupulously honourable way and we did not act up to a high standard. It will be pleaded that business is business. The French did the same to us when they suddenly imposed a quota on British coal and thus exported part of their unemployment to Durham. Durham miners had their own views on this matter and so no doubt had the Danes about the 16% cut.

To sum up, the protection of British agriculture was no easy matter. In a non-expanding market it meant that someone had to be hurt. In this particular case it was the Dane. When the problem got involved with the Empire all kinds of complications arose with such non-Empire exporters as the Argentine as well as with the various Dominions. Discussion ceased to be primarily economic as politics entered in. One thing was quite clear, it was not a purely domestic matter but had infinite ramifications in the outside world. Richardson in the book already mentioned has an excellent chapter which is simply put. It should be read by all. This problem, to what extent a country is able to be master in its own house, has become more urgent of late years. Before 1914 few people realised there was such a problem and would have dismissed the matter without thought. There were many reasons for this, an important one being that it was a rapidly expanding world so that there was room for all. Had the populations of the U.K. and of Western Europe been growing as rapidly between the two wars as they grew in the last decade of the 19th century the problem of protection for British agriculture might have been easier. There would still have been room for most or all the Danish bacon. Population growth, however, had slowed down. Another reason was that tariff changes were infrequent and relatively moderate compared with the inter-war period. Further there were no such things as quotas and currency devaluation both of which could be violent and drastic in their action. But by 1914 the major industrial and agricultural countries had become very intimately intermeshed so that gear changing demanded timing and touch. It was because both were present that those changing the gears failed to realise it was a delicate affair. This lost world was essentially a world of small movements and small adjustments. It has passed.

The attempt to cope with the problems of the inter-war period especially after 1929 made it more and more abundantly clear that sovereign rights were things which must be used with restraint, the more so because they were used without such restraint and indeed were employed by many states as a substitute for or a prelude to war. It is this realisation today which is behind Bretton Woods and all the conferences which have been held since. The Marshall Plan is the latest manifestation.

We now turn to what is apparently a purely domestic concern: the policy of full employment. Here at first sight is something which only concerns ourselves and yet it is far from being so. The bitter experience of hundreds of thousands and millions before the late war has made cool discussion difficult.

Full employment is partly a matter of definition. Sir William Beveridge would allow 3% unemployment for the inevitable seasonal changes and changes in industrial demand. Other figures may be a little higher or lower. Little is ever said as to when a man or woman is employable. Thus by lowering the pension qualification to 55 for both men and women large numbers of employable persons in the legal sense would disappear. Nor is anything said as to the quality of the worker. That however is not our affair here.

A full employment policy would be a relatively easy matter in say a continent such as North America or even in the U.S. which can produce practically all its own foodstuffs and most of the major raw materials. So also with the U.S.S.R. which covers so vast an area. The problem for them would be practically a domestic one but for the United Kingdom such is not the case as a high proportion of our foodstuffs and raw materials must be imported. These can only be paid for by manufactured exports or such invisible exports as the tourist trade and shipping. Whether we can export and how much will depend upon whether we can produce the right type of commodity at the right price. Let the export trade sag and unemployment will appear.

Here, however, we might pause to consider certain latent assumptions which are very important. First it should be noted that unemployment is a luxury which only relatively well-to-do communities can afford. Where a community is really impoverished it cannot afford to have men and women idle. Half a loaf is better than no loaf, and even a quarter of a loaf is better than none. Between the wars the large volume of unemployment

E*

was possible because the remainder of the community kept the
unemployed. If the whole community had been greatly impoverished, as in India, then all would have had to work. Sir
William Beveridge when he talks of full employment does not
say what will be the real wages. That will depend upon the
productivity of industry. It may be high or low according as
men work and are organised: whether they are efficient compared
with others selling in the same international market. At present
the standards of all classes in Great Britain are being maintained
above their efficiency levels by the various overseas loans, by
selling out foreign investments and by shipping gold. There
will come a day when these props will have gone and then the
real incomes will depend as already said upon efficiency.

Now efficiency in industry depends upon (1) managerial
ability, (2) capital equipment and (3) efficient labour. In a
dynamic and ever changing industrial and commercial world
there must be a high degree of flexibility. That, however, is
not enough. Supposing a country is organised, for the moment,
satisfactorily. The pattern will include industries working
for the home market, by far the larger group, and industries
working for export. All goes well until something happens
abroad. Foreign demand falls or ceases. It may be temporarily
or permanently, and it is important to know which, though that
cannot be ascertained easily or quickly. There is unemployment in the export trades and that will react through the fall of
purchasing power among those unemployed and the fall in
demand for certain home produced raw materials or goods by
the exporting factories upon a host of secondary industries. The
unemployed can be maintained temporarily upon out-of-work
insurance benefit, but even that is using up capital for they are
consuming without producing. If, however, the slump continues the labour must be transferred. Where, will depend upon
whether the fall is considered to be temporary or permanent.
If temporary, some sort of public work may suffice, though not
all workmen wish to do such work, but if permanent then
into a new industry. We shall see that it is possible to export
unemployment. The French did it when they put a quota on
Durham coal: we when we limited the import of Danish bacon.

It is this problem of how to stop unemployment being exported which lies at the root of the full employment policy of our country, in particular as we more than any other are dependent upon overseas supplies of food and raw material. As has been said above it is always possible to find employment if no attention is paid to the standard of living, but most people in this country when talking of full employment couple it with a standard at least as good as that already existing. Further, being British they do not expect to be directed.

Full employment then is something we cannot legislate for as a purely domestic thing: all we can do in such a case is to devise as good an unemployed insurance scheme as we can. Full employment must be coupled with international schemes which aim at maintaining as steady a world demand as possible. Can we control the trade-cycle? The Americans really thought they could just before 1929 when they found they couldn't. Worse, they passed their trouble on to the rest of the world for the U.S. is the industrial colossus and when anything goes wrong there the rest of the world is immediately affected. The trade cycle can only be controlled internationally. It was for that purpose that the International Monetary Fund and the International Bank for Reconstruction and Development was founded. It is for the same reason that the Marshall Plan was put forward.

This is a difficult subject and the reader is recommended to turn to Dr. Barna's chapter 'Domestic Economic Policy and International Trade' in *Britain and Her Export Trade*. It is a very persuasive chapter and makes things look easy. They might be if we humans weren't human. Dr. Allan G. B. Fisher develops the problem much more fully and dispassionately in his book *International Implications of Full Employment in Great Britain*. It is a difficult book for the layman but brings out the technical difficulties which are enormously great. That's no reason why both full employment and the international plans should not be studied and implemented but it will take a generation of experimentation before anything really good can be devised. Plans for controlling the world straight off the board are bound to be faulty. We have a lot to do, not least to modify our ideas about the sovereignty of the State.

CHAPTER VIII

PATTERNS OF INDUSTRY

In every country at any given time there exists a 'pattern' of industrial activity, taking the word industry in its wide sense of all human activity. This pattern is ultimately connected with the size and distribution of a country's population, and indeed they are so organically interdependent that any separation of the two, however necessary for exposition, must be regarded as a dangerous necessity. For it is obvious that a community can only exist if it produces, while the amount and type of· production will affect numbers, distribution and consumption.

The term pattern is used loosely, and must not be taken to imply a carefully planned affair, though there exists no modern community which does not exhibit some effects of planning. But most communities are rather like Oriental carpets, whose design and colour are the outcome of centuries of gradual change and adaption. Where the designing has been deliberate and without reference to mellowing, it is always crude and ugly, whether in the case of carpets or communities. There is no one pattern, though certain types are roughly similar, nor is any pattern perfect. At the best it will contain many blemishes, as does a true Oriental rug. If you find a rug which is without flaw you know some European has been organising it.

These patterns are the outcome of long continuous evolution, though now and then sudden and drastic interferences may have taken place. This happened in Great Britain during the Industrial Revolution, when a new design was suddenly introduced. That is why one finds two Englands—one where most people have to live and work, ugly though moderately sanitary, and the other which we reserve for foreign visitors and ourselves on holiday, which is often termed 'This England'. As I write I look out upon some of this old England which is so soul-satisfying, but if I turn my head I can see the new England with its 'hut culture'. When the pattern ceases to be relatively homo-geneous, and when what is really a new pattern is suddenly pieced in, then there arise those cultural clashes which can be so disastrous to the spiritual happiness of communities and individuals. But more than this happens, the economic balance is also upset and material progress is hindered. That, quite apart from the economic troubles which arise out of the spiritual ones. It is just as possible to have bad indigestion owing to emotional upset as from eating the wrong type of food.

The economic geographer might consider five types of pattern, though they are not totally distinct one from the other. Let us begin with our own country, the British Isles. This because it is the country we happen to know most about. Most English people imagine that the life of our community is the normal one, and indeed the actions and behaviour of all the rest of the world are measured against it. That 85% of the people should live in towns and earn their living by manufacturing industry, while the major amount of their food-stuffs are imported, was taken for granted, just as much as drinking tea or eating marmalade for breakfast. The standard of living, or rather the standards of living, were taken for granted equally as playing cricket or foot-ball. Though here we should note the 'two nations' with their different cultures. One which drank coffee for breakfast and China tea for tea, and which played rugby and cricket, plus fives: the other which drank Indian tea at all times and played association football, plus a little cricket, though both combined in the marmalade culture and a hearty contempt for all foreigners.

Actually, Great Britain is quite abnormal economically, and all geographers are warned not to take it as the standard of measurement. The excessively heavy urbanisation: the exces-sive dependence upon imports of raw materials and foodstuffs: the standards of living based not upon productivity alone, but on large overseas investments, now unhappily dispersed, are not found elsewhere. Only since the war have people begun to suspect that our economic position is unstable, and indeed is only prevented from collapse by overseas loans. Thus in an area of 121,000 sq. miles live some fifty million people, mostly urban. This great community has evolved largely in the last

170 years, and as an intensely urbanised one in the last 70. The development was based primarily upon cheap power, coal, and cheap iron, backed by the intense vigour of a few inventors and innovators. The tragedy of the Industrial Revolution was that it occurred during a long period of war, 1790–1815, which diverted so much of the Government's time and energy from reform, and also that class distinctions at the time were so strong that the cultured classes in general drew themselves away, leaving a great mass of workpeople to fester in their ignorance and an uprising middle class with an inferiority complex, who only wanted to ape their betters. Two facts stand out in this period of change which have not been sufficiently emphasised. The unusual ignorance of what was happening. It was ignorance as much as greed which helped to make and spoil the new pattern. Ignorance of much which even 'uneducated' people today take for granted. Ignorance of how to begin to deal with disease. Read Defoe's *Journal of the Plague*, which is far too long, but which gives a good picture of man's approach to the problem of disease. Our ancestors in the period 1770–1840 were little better. Ignorance of the evils of child labour. Ignorance so deep that seeing was not believing. So Robert Owen not only cried out, but demonstrated in vain. Many went to see, but few believed. In the making of patterns, ignorance is always the major part of the background. Today we are merely cleverly ignorant. The second is that our ancestors were imposing upon the masses, without knowing it, what could be called a 'five year plan', only it was a 'seventy year plan'. Out of their poverty they were squeezing the capital for the capital goods which made later Victorian and Edwardian so relatively prosperous. That the techniques and tempo were often faulty is obvious—now. To an age ignorant of such things, they did as best they could. Remember they were vastly ignorant. Much later, when Florence Nightingale began the modern nursing organisation upon which this country prided itself, she did so after going to Germany to learn how.

Gradually the pattern evolved. The great staple industries on the coalfields. The cotton industry in Lancashire at its height before the first war exporting almost 6,000 million square

yards a year to all the world. The great woollen industry of
Yorkshire, with lesser ones in the West and in Scotland. The
ship-building industries of the Clyde, the Tyne, Belfast. The
iron and steel industries, with their distributive activities augmented by manufacture, and then the great and ever growing
London, apparently defying the laws of location and sadly
neglected by the geographers until recently. Alongside this,
a depressed agriculture in decline since 1871 and only picking up
slightly after 1895. But for all the rest, until 1914 an ever
expanding industrial world, producing enough not only to live,
but to lend great sums yearly to all with sound credit: London
the financial centre of the world, and the world coming to us
as they now do to the U.S.

The pattern was never static, and maybe as Toynbee asserts
every civilisation contains the seeds of its own decay. Already
competition was asserting itself after 1870, but until the beginning
of the 20th century the U.S.A. was too busy developing her own
vast interior to have much time to take foreign trade seriously,
though she showed her trends in farm machinery and such things
as typewriters. Conservative England had little time for such
stuff. Germany too, after 1872, rapidly drew along but did not
seriously challenge us till the turn of the century.

The period between the wars sees the pattern considerably
altered. The great staples are stagnant or declining, but new
industries based upon modern science are appearing. Here it
is apparent that the initiative comes from Germany and the U.S.
Half a century's success: overseas investments and the desire
to live more easily are making us less eager to work. The old
school tie and the trade union muffler are beginning to strangle
us. For a short time after 1918 overseas investments begin
again, but finally stop, and before the second war we are beginning to live on capital. With the cessation of overseas
investments the pattern of our exports begins to change, though
partly also because of overseas competition. There emerges
then the type of economy which cannot exist on its earned
income, and which only maintains its standards of living by incomes from overseas investments made by its ancestors, and
which relies upon a vast import of raw materials and foodstuffs:

an economy open to world competition, which must sell at world prices. The standard of living cannot, therefore, be dictated beyond a limited point by Parliament, it depends upon the productivity of the worker and the efficiency of his equipment.

The pattern in the U.S. is vastly different. Here is a continent of 3,600,000 sq. miles, embracing almost all types of climate and more richly endowed with minerals than any other continent except Europe. Further, it is a great whole, unbroken by political or fiscal barriers, only recently occupied by a people whose roots hardly go down, except in a few cases in the New England States and the South. This makes for the greatest mobility of labour and capital. Nowhere in the world is the human factor more mobile. The average density is slightly below 45 per sq. mile, which contrasts with 524 for Great Britain and 740 for England and Wales. Nowhere are extensive areas of dense population found as in Europe and Asia. The three major areas of relatively dense population are, (1) the metropolitan area of the Atlantic seaboard, (2) the area stretching from Detroit to Pittsburg and including the cities of Toledo, Cleveland, Buffalo and Youngstown, (3) the upper Lake Michigan area including Chicago and the adjacent cities, and extending from Milwaukee southward to Indianopolis. For the rest there are scattered islands of density such as Los Angeles, San Francisco and St. Louis. Between are great transitional zones. For one accustomed to the congestion of this country, these metropolitan areas, outside the actual urban boundaries, do not appear densely populated. This large population of some 140,000,000, so massive in itself as contrasted with our 50,000,000, is relatively small compared with the size and richness of the territory which it occupies. This fact must never be lost sight of when discussing the U.S.

Though primarily urban, roughly 56%, the U.S. is still the leading agricultural country of the world. As a producer of wheat, maize, cotton, meat, dairy produce, fruits, the U.S. stands out as a giant among pigmies. One thinks of Canada in terms of wheat and timber; of New Zealand in terms of butter or mutton; of Australia in terms of sheep, but the U.S. either leads or comes a good second. Even in wool, and one never

hears of the U.S. as a producer of wool, they are the second producing country, with half the Australian output. In the basic
minerals they dominate the world, just as they do in industrial
output.

It is a good habit to look up the figures for the leading products
of the world, and to make these comparisons. The *League of
Nations Year Book* is excellent for this.

This U.S. pattern is the product of several factors. The
immense size of the country, its great diverseness of climates
and the extraordinary richness of its mineral deposits: the
origin of its people, a mixture of all the European races, who
had to break away from their old traditions in this new uncharted
world, not only of culture, but of techniques: the lack of a
leisured class and the presence of the Puritan tradition—it is not
an accident that cricket is not played in the U.S.—the fact that
until very recently, in spite of slumps, there were always more
jobs than people to do them, so that new techniques and labour-
saving machines were welcomed: that trade unions came late
after the American workman had come to associate wages with
output: the lack of class distinctions made men search for distinction in money making. Human beings are never equali-
tarians, it is only the failures who pretend that. All these things
and more have created that spirit of exaltation which sweeps
them forward in their material progress. Here are a people who
believe in themselves, just as did the Victorians. Morale is not
something confined merely to fighting men. In contrast there
is one outstanding problem among many which has been intruded into the pattern—the negro. It is not the place nor one's
function to discuss that problem here, but in the Southern
States it is a spiritual as well as a material factor which has ham-
pered progress. It is a problem which has a double interest,
for when one looks to a community such as South Africa, one
finds it in an accentuated form, poisoning all the moral and
economic springs of life. The study of the present U.S. and of
its development since say, the Civil War, is an excellent background against which to study the development of Western
Europe and the Eastern countries such as India and China.

Russia is equally interesting, for here too is a vast land mass comparatively lightly peopled, which is very deliberately planned. We have thus two vast continental areas which offer the spectacle of recent opening up away from the old tradition. In one there is a spontaneous development unplanned and relatively free. Whatever one feels, one cannot deny the vastness of the development nor its speed. And this has been done with no five year plans. In the other, the spectacle is equally interesting, even if terrifying. An all powerful Government, completely ruthless and indifferent to suffering, planning on a vast scale. What has been accomplished in the time is something to contemplate with awe, as one contemplates those vast works the pyramids, and at a comparable price in human suffering. The geographer's immediate task, however, is to study what he sees, and here no morals enter in, though his ultimate task is to attempt to find out, to what end, when moral concepts cannot be excluded. It would be as well if alongside of economics we had continued to develop the art of political economy. Then let us turn to the Continent of Europe, preferably as it was before it destroyed itself. As points, one might take Europe in 1914, in 1938 and post war.

The Europe of 1914 presented a picture which today, no doubt, is somewhat rose-tinted to the older generation, but after careful examination it still emerges as a pleasant thing. There had been no universal war since 1815, ninety-nine years relative peace, except of course in the Balkans, which had always been a bear pit. The Balkan peoples could not help fighting and all decent-minded people had no patience for them. The Americans must think the same today about all Europeans. The lesser wars had not seriously interfered with production and progress. The Franco-Prussian war was over in 8 months. France was little damaged, except the capital, where most of the damage was done by the French themselves. The with-drawing armies left the country practically intact. In those years of relative peace the nations had been able to get steadily to work. The railway systems were built, modern industry developed, slowly until the 'seventies, and very rapidly after that. The new German Empire between 1872–1914 developed into a great industrial power. The Ruhr emerges as the power-house,

not only of Germany, but of Western Europe. French development was much slower and technically they lagged far behind,
though in many of the arts of living, as contrasted with the arts
of gaining a living, they were far ahead. The Mediterranean
countries, chiefly for lack of cheap power and lack of good
government, were still backward, though there were islands of
development even here. But all the time there was a steady
improvement in techniques and standards of living. The
relative peace made diplomatic relations such that they could be
carried on decently. Treaties were rarely broken before the ink
was dry: the art of tourist infiltration had not been developed
and the deliberate sabotaging of peace not yet begun. Tariffs
were relatively low, but what was more important, relatively
constant in their application. Quotas, exchange controls,
prohibitions, did not exist. Over much of the continent
personal travel was unrestricted, and such restrictions as existed
were so mild one would not notice them today. Migration was
unrestricted and all who would could go to the New World,
provided they were medically fit. Trade thus developed relatively unhindered during these 100 years. It was multilateral
trading, that ideal for which the Americans are pressing so hard.
The financial side was equally free. Great Britain stood to the
world in much the same position as the U.S. today. She was
the great lender of capital and the great financier. The Bank of
England and London were not only the centre of the British and
financial banking systems, but of the whole world. Except for
the U.S., which had a completely different banking system, the
rest of the world was more or less modelled on the British system.
The Bank gave the lead in crises. There was no need for talk of
international currencies and bankers' conferences. Gold was
the international currency and the leadership of the Bank of
England sufficed. Conferences were unnecessary. This older
world worked easily. That one can go back to it the writer does
not believe. It has been shattered, while the 'atmosphere'
which made it possible has gone. But it was a semi-automatic
world which had promise.

The first world war shook and cracked this great fabric.
It upset the economic and financial relationships, not only

between the European nations themselves, but between the old and new worlds. Great Britain, France, Germany, to mention the three great powers, found themselves with either diminished investment incomes or with none. Germany as the vanquished nation was required to pay large reparations, the economics of which were not properly understood. London had ceased to be the centre of the financial world, and Great Britain was soon to cease to be an exporter of capital. Countries like Italy, poor before the war, were still more impoverished, and the situation was made worse by the U.S. ban on emigration and the fall in the flow of remittances from former emigrants to their old homes. Russia in the throes of revolution had temporarily ceased to count. But the condition of the patient was not fatal, and by 1924 it looked as if the aftermath of the war had been cleared up and that a fresh beginning was being made. The improvement went on steadily until 1929, when came the great blizzard, starting in the U.S., the like of which had never been before. It is still a subject upon which no broad agreement has been reached, but it swept the world. The U.S. was the colossus upon which so much of the world trade depended, so that when she collapsed she dragged the world with her. Look at the trade figures, whether internal or external, for the year 1929, and then for 1932 (the *League of Nations Year Book* for 1932–33 gives them in detail on pages 168–9). The foreign trade has shrunk from a total of 9,496 million dollars to 2,907. The trade of Great Britain dropped to less than 50%; that of Italy to one third. After 1934 came a slow improvement, but much was due to the rearmament in the face of a threatening Germany.

As the result of the actual war shortages and then of the economic breakdown between 1929–33, most of the European nations directed their policies to a greater self sufficiency. The desire to be self contained manifested itself in higher levels of protection: in quotas and in prohibitions. Each country represented itself as taking obviously necessary steps to balance its budget and its trade accounts. Exchange control appeared and was developed, for reasons known to us all nowadays.

Here it is necessary to take note of the new ideologies. The geographer is not concerned with their rightness or wrongness, but he is with their results as they worked out in industry and commerce. Thus Nazi Germany combining the two policies of war and commerce, turned her attention to South Eastern Europe, which could supply food-stuffs and raw materials upon her own terms and without fear of blockade. Fascist Italy followed this lead, though inefficiently and without reference to obvious facts. The 'Battle for Corn' was doomed to failure given the paucity of arable land and the fast growing Italian population. Nevertheless, both policies altered the European pattern to a considerable extent.

Yet when one has marked all these changes, one is astonished to note how industry and trade still ran along the channels cut before 1914. It is a fact worth noting. These were 'natural' channels, to use a dangerous word. Natural at least in the sense that the Suez Canal is now a natural channel. It exists and has been incorporated into the economic system. Any breaking away from these channels could only be done at great expense and loss. Europe paid heavily for these 'unnatural' changes which were only made possible by the new techniques and by hard work, though it should be noted that the standard of living did not go up as might have been expected or only went up slightly. The standard in this country, the depressed areas excepted, did rise, but because overseas investments ceased and latterly we had begun to live on capital.

Such was the position in 1939. Today the economic system of Europe has been shattered, and not only of Europe, but that connecting Europe with the outside world. As has been said, it is not the physical damage, grave or terrible though it is, which is the major evil, but the destruction of all those delicate and invisible threads which bound the world together. Let us consider the economic damage first. In Great Britain the loss of our overseas investments is the outstanding fact. This country had ceased to maintain itself after 1930 in its earned income, and after 1937 was drawing on capital. If one takes the present value of money, we should have had a deficit in our trade balance comparable with that of today but for our fore-fathers' investments. Germany has been shattered. Those who have seen the German towns need no telling. That the

German people asked for it is not the point here.   It is impossible for them to produce unless their factories and towns are rebuilt.   The Ruhr is shattered.   It must be seen to be believed, but until very recently it was doomed by a policy which aimed at eliminating practically all the heavy industry.   Imagine an equally shattered Midlands in this country, with dismantling commissioners still going round, and ask how it would affect British production.   Without the Ruhr, Germany cannot function: without Germany, Europe must limp along.   It is impossible to reconstruct Europe without Germany.   That is the dilemma.   France was also heavily damaged, though to nothing like the extent of Germany, and yet buildings destroyed or damaged totalled twice that of the first war, while at the same time they were more vital, being factories and urban sites. France too had been greatly impoverished by German exploitation.   Peninsular Italy, always poor, was ruined.   Such damage, grave in itself, could in time be remedied.   Twenty years could see much replaced if the problem were merely physical.   It is more.   The economic threads have been snapped, the channels have not only been blocked, but in many cases destroyed, while the fabric of human values which permitted men to co-operate and work has been so torn to pieces that it will take long to re-weave; it is beyond patching.   Here we come to ideologies which must be discussed elsewhere.

But we must go still further afield in our investigation, taking as types India and China, whose patterns are very different from those in Europe, though similar to one another.   We will deal with India chiefly, with allusions only to China.   India is a great area, 1,500,000 sq. miles, with a population of over 400,000,000.   China is even larger but with about the same size population.   Here are great densities, though if one takes the average density of what was once called British India it was equal to that of France: while that of the Indian States was roughly the same as Spain.   One would not call either country densely populated, but only about 25% of China is capable of cultivation, and what a Chinese cannot cultivate, cannot be cultivated.   The percentage is somewhat higher in India, but we must deduct much of the great mountain areas, the Thar, and allow

for the semi-arid areas.   In Bengal the average density is about
650 to the square mile.   Almost as high as in England, but with
this difference, Bengal is, except for Calcutta and a few minor
towns, a rural country, feeding itself from its own land and with
its own labour.   True it buys a little food, but very little.   Here
in India are peoples living on an ultra-thrifty level, and yet a
large percentage never getting enough to eat.   It is an interesting
fact that civil prisoners in India always put on weight.   Watch
these people and see how little they have of everything.   The
riches of the Indies is one of those fables based upon ignorance.
How can these people save to develop modern industries?
At least 75% are agriculturists, cultivating small patches of
ground, chiefly with hard labour, and very simple inplements.
Here you may see the ploughman 'wending his weary way'
home with his plough over his shoulder; for the rest they rely
largely upon the mattock.   A land of villages, so that the study
of India begins in the villages which, though much modified near
the larger towns and railways, are still very primitive.   One
sees them from the train, generally perched upon a slight rising
or eminence marked by clumps of trees.   If one should visit
them they give the impression of poverty and untidiness, for they
are built of mud and the Indian villager is never tidy though he is
not dirty, as often alleged.   Personally he is clean, as clean as his
inadequate environment permits: it is only collectively that he
is dirty and unhygienic, but were not we until the 19th century;
and did not we make some interesting discoveries among some of
the recruits, male and female, in the late war?   It is difficult to
be clean without three things, laid-on water, drainage and soap.
All relatively modern things.   One remembers Macaulay's
description of the Russian embassy, also the book on behaviour
for the princesses of the royal house of Bourbon, in which it
was laid down that they should not pick vermin off their persons
when visitors were present.   And has not one picked vermin
off oneself when the water and soap were long wanting in the
Flanders trenches.   One remembers too the phrase 'la crasse
latine'.   This perhaps is not quite economic geography, though
it opens up vistas for the soap manufacturers and those who
cater for public as well as private cleanliness.   Nevertheless in

India the poverty is outstanding. Only in such a country can we fully understand that 'the curse of the poor is their poverty'. It makes planning for modern development almost impossible, though nothing is impossible with faith.

But behind this great poverty lie certain facts, material and spiritual, and of these the spiritual are by far the most important. The Hindu religion which is the dominant religion of India, is, as already mentioned, a pessimistic one. A geographer might do well to investigate the relationship between religious belief and work. Further, the veneration of the cow and the reluctance to kill any animal makes animal breeding almost impossible and militates against better farming and cultivation. Finally, poverty to the Indian is not a shameful thing as it is with us. Most Indians in their hearts have a veneration for poverty. The sadu and fakir, religious mendicants, are the ideal. It was this side of Gandhi which appealed to the masses as much as anything else. Not all Indians are Hindus, about 80,000,000 are Mahomedans, who have a very wholesome respect for this life: 50,000,000 more are out-castes or more politely scheduled castes and are pretty open minded about many things, though being human they are snobs and wish to imitate their betters by copying their faults. Certain others, like the Parsees, are very European minded. All these beliefs and cultures have militated against material progress and still do. Finally one comes up against the problem of population density. Here the Malthusian statements still hold true. Relatively to the means of production, India is overcrowded. The balance between population growth and production is maintained by the negative control of death. There is no doubt that if, by a miracle, India could be endowed overnight with equipment and techniques equivalent to those of the U.S., the 400,000,000 could live at a much higher standard than they do, but not at the American standard. The Bombay plan to raise productivity and the standard of living is in itself a good idea, but whether it will succeed will depend, among other things, upon population growth. If by a second miracle, the death rate in India were reduced to that of this country, it would precipitate a food and industrial crisis in a very short time. India's problem here, like that of China and Japan, is gravely difficult. We Europeans had good fortune to help us in our development. Rich fertile country, compare the 15% of available land in Japan with the average for Western Europe; very rich mineral deposits: and with the industrial change, great empty worlds in the Americas and Australasia to take the spill of the populations. A developing Asia finds itself densely crowded before it begins: mineral deposits are only moderate, while there are no empty lands to take the surplus populations. Only by population control can these countries hope eventually to solve their problems, and this is a long period solution.

So far one has sketched hastily and roughly the different patterns one finds. It is quite useless approaching the study as if all countries are alike, all peoples alike and all cultures alike. Yet this is done tacitly by most elementary books on the subject. How can one ignore the veneration of the cow in India: the cow cult among certain African peoples: the ideologies of communist Russia or 'the English way of life'. All these things affect vitally and intimately the economic activities of the peoples.

So far we have considered our patterns rather as they fit into and are part of the cultural background, though it is not a simple case of cause and effect. The relationship is functional. Now we must narrow our enquiry. Why do we find industries where we do find them? Is it accident or can we explain. Here is a factory: How did it get there? Did it just grow like Topsy? Yet whatever Topsy may have thought, most people would insist that she had parents. No one believes in spontaneous generation of babies. The anthropologist and the sociologist would have had much to say about Topsy, though no doubt much would have been lacking and much wrong. So with 'localisation'. Being inherently scientists, and so believing in cause and effect, we are bound to believe there is an explanation. It may not be available in full, but no doubt it exists.

The 'theory of localisation', if we dare to use such a term, is an attempt at such an explanation. Let it be said at once that there is not a 'theory' in that there exists an accepted explanation. There are and have been attempts to formulate a theory, but so far with a qualified success. One thing, however, may be claimed as a result of the past twenty years' work, if there is no generally accepted theory, many of the old fallacies have been exposed and some ground has been cleared. The serious study of the subject is comparatively recent, forced upon us partly by the practical problems of war, and partly because as industrial development proceeded and economic thought developed, there were some flagrant Topsies who needed a lot of explanation.

It is easy to dismiss the subject by taking a few simple and strong cases, as one does in school, but even there an alert child can ask difficult questions. Certain cases are obvious: the extractive industries. Coal can only be mined where Nature has put down coal, so that coal-mines and mining villages are easily explained. The building of ships, at least big ships, must be at the water's edge, where they can be launched. Lancashire used to be an excellent example too. It was one of the articles of geographical faith above dispute, like the height of Mount Everest, 29,002 ft., like the population of China which, whatever might happen, is always 400,000,000: like Redditch, which immediately brings the reflex needles. Alas, for these dogmas, which like so many others have proved false. Which of my generation was not shattered when he learned that Wellington did not cry 'Up guards and at 'em' and that Waterloo was not won entirely on the playing fields of Eton? But if these old beliefs are exploded, others arise to take their place. Myths the human race must and will have. We all know why the Lancashire cotton industry is where it is: the damp winds blowing from the west, which prevented the threads snapping: proximity to the Mersey estuary which faced the supplies of raw material. All very definite and obvious, but Professor Jewkes rather chills one: "Given the establishment of the industry here (Lancashire) and the reasons for the early settlement appear to have been slight, the external and internal economics of a growing industry, combined with the presence of a suitable climate, a convenient port and coal supplies, are sufficient to explain its existence and development". (Jewkes, *Localisation of the Cotton Industry*, Economic History, Vol II, 1930). That is granted Topsy's parents, her statement about herself becomes less inaccurate, but why did it start? The river estuary. There are three such facing west: the Clyde, the Mersey and the Severn.

The moist winds: the Clydeside can be moist enough, while the Severn region is not entirely arid. Further, in the very early days, the cotton did not come from the Southern States, the estuaries were not facing in quite the right direction. Those who read economic history, a useful habit, though one like introspection, which, if abused, can become dangerous, will remember that Robert Owen made his fortune in cotton manufacture at New Lanarkshire, not in Lancashire. There are still a few cotton mills up there. Why was there no cotton industry in and around Bristol? Why did it languish and almost die out in New Lanarkshire? One doesn't really know. Then if one looks away from Lancashire to the Continent, one finds cotton industries often in very wrong places. There is for instance Roanne in France, tucked upon the Loire valley on the edge of the Massif. This one discovered about 2 a.m. while in a moribund condition, when travelling in a French omnibus train, but on being told that they spun and wove cotton goods, one was galvanised instantly into violent economic life. It was all against the teaching one had recently acquired. Nevertheless, there it was, spinning and weaving cotton, in spite of the economists and Lancashire. One must start again. Maybe the economic and human factors accounted for it. Bristol was an old manufacturing centre with strongly entrenched craft guilds, which did not welcome innovators. Remember Watt might not have been able to get on with his steam engine had not the University of Glasgow allowed him to work within its precincts away from the hostility of the guilds, which resented an unskilled man infringeing their privileges. Lancashire was outside of these guilds and their regulations, but later why, to repeat the question, did the cotton industry fade away from the Clyde? Because, we are told, the great shipbuilding industry and its ancillaries took up all the attention, capital and labour of the people: surely not. There can't be supplies of strong male labour without considerable supplies of female labour as well, and also of males not sufficiently strong for the heavy industries, and high profits will always draw capital. No, that won't do. Maybe then it is because people tend to think in grooves. That in a prosperous Lancashire the line of least resistance mentally and industrially is, or rather was, cotton, while in the Clyde it is the heavy engineering industries. There we will leave it for the moment unsolved.

Perhaps after all it is just chance. When the Royal Commission was conducting its enquiries just before the war, it got some queer answers. One successful industrialist, when asked why he put his factory where it was, replied because it was as near his favourite golf course as possible. Another, because his wife refused to live further than a certain distance from London—a cogent reason, as all we married men know. What a history could be written on such a theme. Again, let us ask a question. The Morris Works at Cowley are the accidental result of Lord Nuffield being born at Oxford. Suppose he had been born at Cambridge. Would the factories to be have been built at Grantchester? Heaven forbid. Let us rejoice that Providence decided as it did, in spite of benefactions lost. Suppose he had been born at Truro. Would the Morris cars have streamed out of Cornwall? Here are some problems. On the other hand, many factories have been placed after careful thought and calculation, the Ford for instance. One can't imagine golf influencing the Ford executive. Perhaps the Commission should have called certain others to give evidence, whom it forgot. Those who started business and factories and who went bankrupt. You see the golfer had done very well: the uxorious manufacturer also had combined profit with bliss: Morris had been an outstanding success. Was it that they just struck lucky or is there more behind it? Weber in his *Theory of Location*, attempts to reduce the problem to one of transport costs, but is compelled to make a series of assumptions and simplifications which are open to serious criticism. Dennison in his *Location of Industry and the Depressed Areas*, pages 9–18, discusses briefly Weber's theory and conclusions. "It certainly seems that Weber's assumptions are such that the theory does not give an adequate explanation of locational factors: neither does it provide a means to undertake a study of particular problems. There is, at the outset, an arbitrary assumption in that the first step is to select certain factors as the only factors which need to be considered", and "There is a second serious limitation which develops in analysing the working of the chosen locational forces. This is the removal of the analysis from the world of costs and prices, which is the economist's field, in order to formulate it in terms of technical co-efficients". He concludes: "Weber's theory, being little more than an elaboration of certain assumptions which, although they may be applicable to some cases, and not of the 'general' scope which he intended, cannot thus be used for the analysis of all locational problems. Indeed, the most obvious fact which has emerged since the theory appeared is its slight value for the study of particular problems", and in a footnote he adds: "Some of the factors determining the location of the heavy industries of the 19th century can be analysed by Weberian methods; there are, in fact, frequent indications that he was thinking largely in terms of such industries". There, one thinks, is the essence of the criticism of such an approach as Weber's: the desire to over-simplify the problem and to think in terms of transport only, whereas human resistances and economic frictions are vastly important. For some of the massive industries, transport costs can be very important, and one is inclined to think that Dennison underestimates their importance in some other cases. They can be vastly important in the secondary industries when competition is very keen and profits depend upon fine margins. None the less, in a great range of light industries, where material counts for a small part of the cost, there is a complex of cost factors which together determine location. No one is dominant. We have already seen how complex a thing a transport charge can be.

There is no doubt that the labour factor plays a very important role. The older economists used to assume the mobility of labour, both from place to place, and from industry to industry; an assumption which has its uses, provided always that one remembers it is an assumption. In actual fact it is never fluid, even at the best. Labour does not flow, it creeps. Lack of housing, unwillingness to leave one's friends, and the friendly environment, make for differences in labour costs. Labours' attitude to work and the techniques are equally important. It is this fact which makes the 'direction of labour' so difficult in this country. A planned economy in a dynamic world must imply movement of industry and so of labour. Communist Russia realises this and sends the labour as one sends a soldier. In this they are logical. It is we who are illogical when we desire planning but limit direction. Maybe the Russians are wrong too, as it is yet to be proved that life can be directed by formal logic and the syllogism.

It would appear then that the forces making for localisation are many and complex. Some can be estimated roughly, such as transport, costs of land, the incidence of taxation, and even labour charges, but many are very indirect and intangible. Many industrialists have insisted that transport charges have been a minor factor with them, but that time has been important. Nearness to their markets, so that goods can pass from the factory to the consumer very quickly. How does one assess time and convenience? Many of these tangibles are wrapped up in that bundle of facilities which the economists call 'external economics'. The shrewd business man can sense these things and come to his decision without being able to explain it. But he can make mistakes. More we cannot say at the moment. Let us go back now to our earlier examples. The golfing industrialist and the others could make their decisions and succeed because these diverse factors allow of a good deal of play. In the past one has tended to think of localisation too much as a pin-pointing business, such as Redditch or Lancashire. If we had looked outside of our country we should have been less sure. One must think of localisation in terms of regions. So long as a factory or an industry is put down within a given area—which may be quite extensive—all will be well. That explains the cotton industry in Roanne, the Morris works at Oxford. The latter would probably have succeeded equally well in Cambridge, but I doubt about Truro. I think young Morris would have found things hanging fire down there, and would probably have moved away. This explanation allows for apparent accident in localisation, but the accident can only happen within the given locus to be successful. Let us return to the statement in the first paragraph, that the pattern of industry is intimately connected with the size and distribution of population. One might go further, and say they are aspects of the same phenomenon, That is important, as it means we are never free to plan as if a country were yet untouched. Imagine the planners coming along with their blue prints, their Town and Country Planning Act and, if you like, their nationalisation schemes, or if you don't, the alternative non-planning blue prints. They are coming not today, but in the Roman invasion fleet. Behind them are the 50,000,000 present inhabitants: the bull-dozers are all ready and everything else in the form of capital goods we haven't got yet. What could we not do? But that won't happen. More than a thousand years of settlement, of work good and bad lie behind us. The great towns are there: one can't unscramble London or them. The people have a long past history which affects their outlook and behaviour. Think of what mining might be if the psycho-analysists could release all the repressions and untangle all the complexes of the miners, and of some others. The planners are too clever and too stupid. They have blue prints for the material side: none for the human. Today we can only hope to modify things slowly, and by the time we are ready to realise the present blue prints they will be obsolete. Localisation must therefore be partly explained in terms of the past, both on the material and non-material side, together with those other factors to which we have alluded. Behind the obvious explanations of facts there are always others which are unseen in their working and effects. Government tariff policies are certainly important, both positively and negatively, while all the subtle reactions upon one another of these forces which come into the calculations when studying the Theory of International Trade, must be allowed for. The fact is that we have not the time to trace things back to their sources. We go back just a step or two, and then stop.

Reading is not easy to recommend. There is Dennison's *Location of Industry and the Depressed Areas*, published in 1939. This is the most thorough study of the subject from the academic standpoint. It is not easy reading for the beginner. Perhaps the best beginning would be *The Memorandum on the Location of Industry* by Professor J. H. Jones. This is one of the Appendices in the *Royal Commission on the Distribution of the Industrial Population* (Cmd. 6153 of 1940). It is quite a considerable thing of some 30 pages, and is divided into two chapters. The first chapter can be read by all: the second is more difficult but should be attempted. The Report itself is worth looking at and dipping into. There is also the *Report on the Localisation of Industry* by P.E.P., published a few months before the Government one. This has some very useful tables. Thus Appendix I, 'The Regional Distribution of Industry in Great Britain, gives a complete analysis of industry by Regions (one should note that these are Government made regions and not P.E.P.). Total figures of employed are given first, and then are broken up between the regions. Below in italics is the 'Location Factor' which is best ignored for the moment. It is a complicated idea and will help none but the mathematically-minded. Chapter II 'The Present Location of Industry' has diagrams which are useful, and on page 39 a large full page one which again may or may not help. There are also more diagrams on the following pages. Weber's book is not recommended.

CHAPTER IX

THE MECHANISM OF EXCHANGE

ECONOMIC geography as we have already seen is always borrowing from economics to a greater or less extent and there are times when the economist has to explain personally. This is one of those occasions. The reader would be well advised to read up money in one of the many text books. There is an enormous literature on money and yet it is difficult to recommend a small book. The fault lies not with the authors but with the task they are set. Small books are very cramping. Three suggestions are made. Cairncross *Introduction to Economics* has chapters on money which are very straightforward. Parts V and VI deal with International Trade and Money. It is a good book to start on. This should be followed by Robertson *Money* in the Cambridge Economic Handbooks. A good book though it demands careful reading. Finally *What everyone wants to know about money* by "Nine Economists from Oxford" is very useful and has a bibliography at the end. It is not too simple but one cannot go beyond a point in simplifying. What will be said in this short chapter is mostly by way of comment and cannot be a systematic exposition.

Whether the buying or selling is internal or external does not matter; goods and services are bought and sold for money. The difference between home and foreign trade lies in the fact that for home trading only one currency is involved. There is no problem similar to that of the foreign exchange which arises out of the fact that two or more currencies are employed. At home the major interest is to maintain as stable a price level as possible, as fluctuating price levels mean that some sections of the public are disappointed in their rightful hopes and expectations. Rapidly changing values cause unrest and industrial friction, make planning difficult and discourage saving. All this we know only too well today. The maintenance of a steady price level is today one of the duties and functions of a government and in this they act largely through the Central Bank. In this business of currency management certain techniques of measurement such as index numbers and techniques of control involving the quantity theory of money are employed. These we must glance at.

Foreign trade on the other hand while benefiting from stable currencies is further complicated by the fact that two or more currencies are employed and some method of changing one into the other has to be devised and employed. Today this is not easy now the common international currency gold has ceased. It might be as well here to dispose of a small point: that foreign trade is only a modern form of barter, British cars and machinery against, say, wheat and butter, This is incorrect: barter is the direct exchange of goods for goods without the intervention of money or even the idea of money being present. It is a primitive way of life which if adhered to condemns a people to remaining primitive.

What do we understand by the term money? Most people think they know what money is, and so they do up to a point, though soon they get out of their depth and are apt to make dangerous generalisations. Even the economists do not always agree in their definitions, though that does not matter much so long as each person's definition is clearly made and understood. Is a shilling, a pound note, a cheque, money? Most people would say yes, though a little thought will make one hesitate about cheques. There are places which will not accept them. Cheques have been known to be returned. People take shillings and pound notes without question, though only in Great Britain in the case of shillings, and even the pound note has not the hearty welcome abroad that its father, the sovereign, had. Further, silver is only legal tender up to forty shillings. Taking all these considerations together, we may say that money should be immediately acceptable and without question. Anything which fulfils that condition is money. Cigarettes in Germany? Certainly they are or were currency, though one would hesitate to call them money as they were not universally accepted. Like the cheques, there were places where they would not pass. What would constitute an international money? In the good old days there was no talk about an international currency, because there was one. People don't talk much about what they've got but what they lack. Up to 1914, gold, whether as coin or bullion, was the international currency. The sovereign was welcome not because it was a sovereign, but because it was a certified ingot of gold which weighed a definite amount, just as the Englishman was welcomed not so much because of his blue eyes as because of his yellow sovereigns. Today the dollar is the most valued international money. Dollars can be counted on to buy things and can even be turned into gold: pounds cannot.

The definition therefore must always be qualified. Money under certain conditions. When there is no hesitation the thing can be called money. Where people hesitate, as in the case of a cheque, it is better called a 'medium of exchange' which is a wider expression.

Money may for certain purposes be regarded as a kind of ticket which gives you the right to things. It was Carlyle, wasn't it, who said that a man with sixpence was a king: he could command the services of men and goods—up to sixpence, but it is more than a ticket. Its effect upon production is not so simple as that. The relationship is functional. That is why a disordered currency can cause so much damage. It is like poor or bad blood which affects the whole health and well-being of the body.

This further relationship is due to the very minute division of labour and our mutual interdependence on society. Here is a workman laying bricks: here a bank clerk: here a teacher. Their work has no meaning except in terms of society. They have agreed to do their work on the tacit assumption that the tickets which they receive can be exchanged for definite amounts of things they want. That is, they expect money to act as a measure of value. This is important. Accurate measurement which is the basis of all our scientific world. What does 1/1,000 part of an inch matter? Watt and his mechanics didn't worry about things like that. The modern engineer wouldn't get far if he didn't. Money is used as the basis of our social, industrial and commercial measurements. It ought to be accurate. That, by the way, is a reason why so much economic reasoning is faulty. It is based upon a yardstick which is doubly inaccurate: (1) the measure itself fluctuates violently and (2) there are many things in life which can not be so measured.

The first thing then would appear to be to find some way of measuring changes in the value of money. Rather like the calculations which are made for the expansion and contractions in metals or the corrections which must be made when navigating a plane on a dark and windy night. For that purpose index numbers have been devised, but index numbers are delicate and tricky things. Irving Fisher in his book on Index Numbers had as many methods of calculating them as there were days in the year, which meant that at the best they were relative to the particular purpose for which they are devised, which they are, or that we were not quite clear as yet how to make and employ them, which again is partly true. More will be said of index numbers shortly.

In addition there must be also a clear idea of how the value of money is determined. All this is well presented in Robertson's book, chapters II and III, and leads up to what is called the Quantity Theory of Money. This theory can become involved but certain simplifications may be made for the beginner.

The theory arises out of a peculiarity of money which distinguishes it from all other commodities. It is useless in itself. That is why we may liken it to a ticket. Tickets are of no use in themselves. Bus tickets without a bus don't carry one far. A pound note after all is merely a piece of paper. It might be objected that a sovereign was useful in itself, which is true. It was a ticket made of gold, a rather expensive thing to do. If, however, you were given the option of being marooned upon a desert island for six months with £500 in sovereigns or £500 of food and other things, there is no doubt which you would choose. The point is one cannot eat, drink, wear or do anything else with money. It only has value when spent. You receive it only because you believe it can be passed on again. From this arises an important fact. Contrast money with commodities. Sugar one eats and while we would like the ration increased we would not thank the Government for a tenfold increase. Bread is for eating, clothes for wearing. One suit we greatly need: two we also greatly desire but who wants fifty suits? There was a certain Marquis of Anglesey who had hundreds of suits and fancy waistcoats but he undoubtedly needed to visit a psycho-analyst. We are thinking of normal men, so far as we know what normal means.

In the case of commodities the law of diminishing utility acts sooner or later and more or less strongly. What is called the elasticity of demand varies from individual to individual and from one commodity to another. That is what makes giving a Christmas present so difficult to a man, having got one wallet and a pair of house-slippers the value in use of a second of these is almost zero. With money, however, the elasticity of demand is straightforward. The value of money varies inversely with the supply. Double the quantity of money in a given com-munity, other things remaining the same, and the value of money will be halved. Halve the amount of money and its value will double. Take a simple example. Imagine a com-pletely isolated community with a given standard of living, a given price level and a given amount of money with which to do its business. A miracle happens and everyone wakens up one morning with exactly twice the amount of money they had and everybody knows it has happened to all. The money only has doubled: the community is no better off as it has no more goods. Either prices will double if the money is to be employed or the money could be left idle while people trade at the old prices. Do not imagine for a moment that the quantity theory has been explained by this ultra-simple example. There is more in it than that, but the germ lies there. A community only requires a certain amount of money to perform a given amount of busi-ness at a given price level. The rest of the theory has to do with all the frictions which one meets in real life, and with the func-tionally reactions which would take place. If prices are doubled as a result of inflation and then after a lapse of time are brought back to the original level it does not follow that everything will be as it was.

It follows from the quantity theory that the amount of money circulating in a community is of great importance. If production should go up 10% then, to keep prices level, the quantity of money should be increased by the same amount and vice versa. Who looks after this business of keeping the price level all right? Before 1914 it was left to itself pretty much: between the wars the central banks co-operating with their respective governments tended more and more to try to control it with qualified success. Today in this country the Government does it through the Bank of England and the Treasury.

There is one last point to which attention should be drawn in connection with the Quantity Theory. We have seen that, should the quantity of money be doubled while the amount of goods to be exchanged remains constant, prices will double. It is equally true that if the quantity of money remains constant while the supply of goods halves prices will double, but it makes a vast difference to the community whether prices have doubled for the first or second reason. In the second case the community has been impoverished.

The measuring of the price level is done by means of index numbers, an account of which will be found in Robertson's book, or if the reader prefers in Cairncross's *Introduction to Economics*, chapter 26. Which is the more useful will depend upon the reader. It is often a good idea to read two explanations as one always helps to elucidate the other.

Index numbers imply enough mathematics to worry many non-mathematical minds. This statement will astonish the real mathematician and statistician, but we needn't mind their feelings. For those who are not calculators, the simple explanations of Cairncross will be quite adequate. Where Robertson throws the lever into the reverse, if you are worried, just skip that paragraph.

Index numbers are a device for measuring the change in the value of money, but it may be objected by the ordinary man that prices of goods don't all go up equally so how can you make an accurate measure. The objection is the more serious when one considers patterns of consumption which vary considerably from person to person and from class to class. If everyone consumed identical amounts of the same kind of commodities one might employ an index number with confidence, but they do not.

There was an interesting correspondence in *The Times* some few years after the first war. The first writer asserted that the cost of living of the middle classes (we need not stop here to identify them) had increased threefold. The second denied this, saying that if that were so, middle class incomes would perforce be three times what they were, and they were not. Both writers were at cross purposes. The first writer meant that if a certain group of people whom he called middle class were to live in exactly the same manner as before, consuming identical amounts and qualities of goods and services in 1921 as in 1914, it would have cost them three times the money to do so, which was probably true. The second writer had meant that they were not so living but had altered the pattern of their consumption so that they were spending only 50% more than in 1914. This is important. Accurate comparison can only be with identical patterns of consumption.

That brings us to the term 'the general level of prices' which is supposed to be measured by the published index numbers. The general level of prices might remain constant while individual prices making up the general level might constantly alter. To use Marshall's figure it is like the average height of a forest. Some trees push up: some decay and fall but the general height of the forest remains the same. Is there any use in this general level of prices? Economists think there is, provided the index number is properly constructed, that the user knows at least roughly how it is constructed and that it is used for the proper purpose. Too often index numbers are misused. For special purposes special index numbers will be required. Thus there is a Cost of Living Index which applies to working class incomes. It was discontinued in 1947 and a new one has taken its place. Why was this? Because it had been wrongly constructed? Not at all; in its time it was quite useful, but in the last ten years the patterns of consumption and living have greatly changed. Even a special index number will not apply very accurately to particular persons, and at the moment with all the price controls and interferences one must be very circumspect how one employs them.

While dealing with index numbers which aim at showing

changes in price levels or what is the same thing, in the value of money, we might note that they can be used for other purposes such as measuring industrial production by volume or the change in the volume of the import and export trades—what is often referred to as the 'quantum' of trade. How difficult this can be will be seen if one refers to the article, 'New Index of Industrial Production' in the *London and Cambridge Economic Service* for February 1948.[1] More advanced readers are recommended to look it up. Even beginners might glance at it, for if it is too difficult to read it will at least dispel any idea that these things are simple. The sooner, in this very complex world, people get rid of the idea that things are simple, the better. One's object in stating this is not to dismay but to make people realise that progress in social or industrial organisation can only come through hard and accurate thinking.

Index numbers for the reason above stated cannot be used to make comparisons between different countries. Take a simple example. Very many years ago when comparing the cost of living of 'typical' working class families in Germany and Great Britain, two lists were made, one showing what it would cost a family to live in Germany with the British pattern of consumption and the second showing what it would cost a German family to live in England with the German pattern. The question to be answered was "In which country is the cost of living cheaper for the working man?" The result showed that it was cheaper to live in Germany if one lived the German way and cheaper to live in England if one lived the English way. The reason is obvious. The German pattern of consumption was catered for by the German economic system while the same was true of the English pattern in England. It is no use talking about living being cheaper or dearer until the whole pattern quantitatively and qualitatively has been specified and also the environment in which it is found. So too when comparing different periods and ages. Index numbers are practically valueless for comparison over even half a century as patterns of living have changed so much.

Now let us return to this question of money as a stable and

[1] Bulletin I: Vol. 26: Feb. 18. 48.

steady measure of value. We thought at first sight that any changes in the value of money might be calculated by means of index numbers and regulated with reference to the quantity theory. Here are two techniques which ought to enable us to rectify any tendency to deviate from normal. It appears, however, that these techniques, useful and necessary as they are, will not do what we had hoped. All we can say is that they are useful but they can only be applied by experts and even then they have their limitations. We know much more than we did twenty years ago, but those who construct them are the most cautious in their use. It is the half-baked economist and planner who forces their use.

Still a stable currency is what we desire though there never has been one. The sad thing about it all is that in spite of all our desires and better techniques currencies are less stable than they were in the Victorian period. There is a chart of the price level for the 19th century in Layton's *Introduction to the Study of Prices*. There it will be seen that between 1820 and 1849 prices fell 25%, that is, roughly, 1% a year; between 1849 and 1874, they rose 25%, again 1%; between 1874 and 1896, they fell 40%, about 2%. This period was always held up to us young men as one of catastrophic fall and almost unrelieved gloom. With advancing age one has learned much. The final prewar period 1894 to 1914 shows a 34% rise which is about 1.7% a year. Today we would regard such small changes as indicative of a relatively stable currency. Since then movements have been violent. By 1920 prices had risen to three times the 1913 level but fell very rapidly the next two years. Between 1922 and 1929 they were comparatively stable but fell drastically after that until they were below prewar level after which they began to rise again. During the late war and since there has been a much greater control exercised, thanks to improved techniques. The Board of Trade wholesale figure was 220 in May 1948 with 1930 as 100, though this figure is too generalised. For our guidance it is split up into first the three major groups: Basic materials 301.7; intermediate products 248.9; and manufactured articles 213.2. There is a further and fuller analysis by major articles. But such indices cannot be

F*

applied to retail prices and cost of living where there is so much
interference in the way of fixed and subsidised prices, rationing,
etc.

A stable currency implies some standard of value with which
to regulate and control it just as a proper system of weights and
measures requires that there shall be 'sealed' patterns somewhere
in existence.   If a grocer is accused of giving light weight and
using light weights the accusation would have no meaning if
there were not somewhere a standard pound weight to which
appeal could be made.   So with money, but the business is much
more difficult.   Many standards have been tried, such as the
silver standard, which made silver the measure.   Bi-metallism,
which was an attempt to employ both silver and gold.   Then
gold.   There have been and are variations of the gold standard
varying from the classical English gold standard with sovereigns
in circulation to the gold standards in pre-1914 France, U.S.,
and Germany down to the post war gold bullion standard of this
country which was introduced in 1925 and broke down in 1931.
The U.S. is still on the gold standard though the gold content of
the dollar is not what it was.   There is also the Gold Exchange
Standard.   Finally, we come to the modern though by no means
new unconvertible paper currencies which attempt with more or
less success to maintain a standard of value by means of techniques which employ elaborate methods of control—controlled
currencies of which ours is one.   We need only refer to the Gold
Standard and manipulated currencies.

Keynes once said that the gold standard was a barbaric one
for it linked the unit of value with a metal the supply of which was
dependent upon luck.   That was true but luck held during the
19th century.   Perhaps, though, the fact that it was barbaric
helped it in its success for it operated in a barbaric world.   May
I suggest that the reader tries to define what is the difference
between a savage and a civilised man.   One's own experience is
that the civilised man is clever mechanically and administratively
but that the savage is more courteous, speaks his language more
correctly and is less ferocious and cruel.

It is likely that had there been no wars and had the world
continued in a steady evolution that the gold standard would

have evolved into some form of controlled and manipulated system. Even before 1914 it was not more than semi-automatic. Under the gold bullion standard, gold coin did not circulate. The gold was in the bank vaults available for its proper purpose as a reserve against various pressures and contingencies and also for export if necessary.

The essence of the gold standard, however modified it might be is, (1) that the local currency, be it dollars, pounds or what, generally circulating in the form of paper, can be converted on demand into gold. Prior to the first war notes were convertible into sovereigns which circulated freely but under the later gold bullion standard only bullion was available and that in minimum amounts: (2) that gold can come and go freely without any interference. This freedom to import or export gold is essential to a gold standard and where it is not found, whatever the name may be, that is not a gold standard country. It is through this inward and outward flow that the price of gold is equalised everywhere and through the gold the different currencies are linked. The amount of the internal currency depended upon the ratio between gold and the credits based upon gold. This ratio was roughly 10:1 in this country and had been arrived at purely empirically. Such being the case the expanding power of the currency was ultimately limited by the amount of gold in the bank vaults. Thus the flow of gold influenced and affected the internal price level.

As most of the world's great industrial and commercial nations had gold currencies or currencies based upon gold, they were all linked together by this common base and so their price levels went up and down together though not necessarily in the same degree. There was an international money, gold, with which debts could be settled, though the movement of gold was relatively slight in a world of multilateral trading and in which there was a relative equilibrium between the total activities of the trading nations.

With gold as the international currency the problem of exchanging one currency into another, of turning pounds into dollars and dollars into francs was easy. All one had to do was to find out the exact weight of pure gold in a gold dollar, a gold

pound, etc. The rest was simple division. The pars of exchange were thus definite fixed rates, for when comparing a gold
sovereign with a gold dollar, mark or franc one was really
comparing gold with gold. The exchange rates could only
fluctuate around this rate by an amount necessary to pack, ship
and insure gold for export or import. These were the gold
points. The stable exchange rates made trading easy.

There is, however, more to it than that. One is told by the
monetary experts that one can have one of two things from a
currency, either stable exchange rates or a stable internal price
level. One can't have both. This was very evident between
the wars though not so evident before 1914 when fluctuations
were of a slight order so that both ends were apparently achieved.

The world which ended in 1914 as has already been said had
witnessed a hundred years of relative peace. It had been a
rapidly expanding world in every way, so that most maladjust-
ments tended to rectify themselves given time. That was why
the trade cycle, serious though it was, could be expected to run
its course in a few years. In this world gold, except for China
and India, was the fundamental money. The gold standard
reigned with slight qualifications. In India the link with gold
was through the Gold Exchange Standard: with China, on a
fluctuating silver basis, the link was maintained by techniques
devised and operated through the Exchange Banks. Gold
flowed as already stated. This smooth working, however, was
dependent upon an industrial and commercial world in equilibrium. One cannot overemphasise the point that a currency
cannot be considered by itself: it is merely a part of a larger
mechanism. That is why present day attempts to establish
sound currencies is so difficult. Whether the new currency in
Germany succeeds or not depends upon whether industry and
production can be stepped up. Currencies cannot work in a
vacuum or partial vacuum. Given the present world chaos the
gold standard would not work and indeed its disappearance is
explained by the chaotic and troubled conditions since 1914.
Prior to that date trade largely balanced. Great Britain and
Western Europe importing foodstuffs and raw materials paid
for them by manufactures and by various 'invisible' items such

as shipping, banking services and interest on investments. Europe was the creditor to the rest of the world and the debtors paid their debts out of surpluses of produce which Europe much wanted. It was a beautiful piece of smooth working mechanism. As all countries balanced their trade except on rare occasions payments were merely matters of financial adjustment made by and through the banks and financial houses. In all this Great Britain was the pivot. In general the world looked to London for a lead in times of crisis and got it. London was the great financial and lending centre. It was a world at peace. The shadow of war was only really evident some few years before war came, at least to most people, and even then caused little dismay as none realised what a modern world war could be like.

It was not a static world. Change was constantly taking place and at an accelerated rate, but it was relatively ordered and not sufficiently swift to disrupt lawful anticipations and hopes. Nor was it a perfect world. How good it was depended upon where one happened to be born and into what class but it was a world with promise and one in which change could have come without disruption. It would be wrong to blame the first war for all the troubles which followed but there is no doubt that war accentuated many tendencies while at the same time it diverted attention and wealth away from construction to destruction. In the reconstruction which followed allowance must be made for ignorance both in high and low places just as it must be allowed for today.

The interim period found Great Britain relatively poorer and the U.S. relatively and absolutely richer: France devastated in the north, Germany defeated but intact though condemned to pay reparations: the Austrian Empire in liquidation and Russia in revolution. All the old financial, industrial and commercial relationships had been torn and disrupted though not to the same extent as today. Sufficiently, however, to make going back impossible.

The salient facts of the situation were first that the creditor-debtor relationship had been reversed. Europe was no longer, except for Great Britain, a great creditor and the U.S. no longer a debtor. That in itself would have made difficulties. Second, reparations which were badly conceived and their economic effects little understood further affected the financial working of this delicately poised world. Third, many countries which had been primarily agricultural turned to manufacture which they proceeded to encourage and develop with high tariffs. Fourth, the fall in the rate of growth of population limited certain kinds of agricultural expansion. It led to a slow deterioration in the farming West of the U.S. and limited expansion in the West of Canada. No longer could one say to a young man, 'Go West, my son', for the supply of wheat was such that prices did not pay the producer. The ratio of exchange had moved against the agriculturalist everywhere. Fifth, the war had left nations fearful of what might happen to them. Neutrals had suffered for lack of commodities and so turned to home manufacture. National feelings had been exacerbated and fear made things worse.

All these forces together made an easy working world impossible while the immediate post war years were naturally engaged in cleaning up the economic debris. It was not merely the material world which was affected, there was ferment in the world of ideas and all the old relationships and loyalties were being challenged. The effects of all this can be studied in the long list of abortive conferences. Though it is not economic geography we would commend Carr's *International Relations between the Two World Wars*, which is an excellent short sketch of what was going on in the immediate background of our economic world affecting it both directly and indirectly.

Let us now return to the inter-war currency problems. The gold standard had broken down except in the U.S. and Scandinavia. Europe including ourselves was working on inconvertible paper currencies which were more or less inflated. In Germany the currency had broken down completely and was providing the economists with some excellent raw material for observation. Russia at the time did not count. These inconvertible currencies, the value of which fluctuated with relation to purely internal influences were now no longer connected one with the other. The exchange ratios had no meaning so that trading became much more difficult as exchange rates could not be easily ascertained while temporary adverse balances could no longer be settled by gold movements. Trading became almost a gamble. At the same time inflation at home and rising prices caused unrest and industrial trouble. Every country suffered in this way, some more, some less. The need for stable currencies was obvious. In this country, return to gold which had worked so well during the 19th century was achieved in 1925 with a much over-valued pound. Not everyone had believed this to be wise. Lord Keynes (then Mr. Keynes) had protested vigorously in his pamphlet *The Economic Consequences of Mr. Churchill*, a brilliant prophecy of what would happen. Today this pamphlet does not seem so impressive read after the event. Not that Mr. Churchill had much to do with it except that he was Chancellor of the Exchequer. It did not follow that he knew much about currencies. The fact was that those in high places in the Treasury and the Bank of England were too set for a fluid world. The reasoning behind the action taken was obsolete and based upon conditions which had ceased to exist. Let us look at them for a moment.

Prior to 1914 if a country, say our own, had overtraded or overlent and thus got into debt, it would have found the exchange rates moving against it until the gold points were reached when gold would flow. This gold came from the Bank of England reserve which was 'the reserve' for the whole system. Ordinarily these movements rectified themselves automatically or semi-automatically but on occasion they were too strong for this and the Bank had to take action. This it could do in a variety of ways but they all resulted among other things in a curtailment of the Joint Stock Banks' credits. They in turn had to reduce their lending and so the volume of money available for industry was reduced and through that the price level was effected, prices fell. If on occasion action was very drastic this might cause depression and unemployment. The opposite would happen if we had been selling abundantly relatively to our buying and prices would rise. The effect in the first case was that falling prices made our country a bad market in which to sell and so imports tended to fall away. Abroad the opposite took place and so the two movements would restore equilibrium. Further the price level of the country was, once more brought into accord with external prices.

This adjustment was, however, only possible provided certain conditions were fulfilled. First, the differences in the value of money had to be slight and in fact the pre-1914 world was, as has been said elsewhere, a world of small adjustments. Second, it had to be possible for these subtle price interactions to be passed on from one group to another which it was before the war, and third, this monetary pressure would tend to lead to a fall in wages and might even result in unemployment. None of these conditions were present after 1918. The inter-war period was one of violent oscillations which did not permit of pre-1914 finesse. Labour, the masters and the professional bodies were so strongly organised that any attempt to pass on the monetary pressure was at once resisted and resulted in strikes and lockouts while unemployment and reduced wages were no longer regarded with a fatalistic eye.

Nevertheless unemployment on a vast scale did occur as it must if these adjustments are not made. That is a lesson which has been forgotten and which must be remembered when applying a full-employment policy together with wage rates which are out of accord with world prices. How far all this distress might have been avoided by greater wisdom and insight it is difficult to say. These troubles and strains were not confined to the United Kingdom and ultimately culminated in the great world break-down which began in 1929, though we did not abandon gold until about the end of 1931. By 1933 most countries had abandoned the gold standard. The two great exceptions were the U.S. which however had compromised and reduced the gold content of the dollar, and France which succumbed in 1936. It is not our purpose here to assess the part played by the various countries in this unhappy period.

What followed was a *suave qu'il peut* which resulted in a series of experiments most of which aggravated matters and which largely destroyed what is called multilateral trading replacing it by unilateral agreements. We are interested here in the monetary arrangements only and so will pass by the tariff manipulations.

Before enumerating these various experiments, one can do little else here, let us remind ourselves what are the central facts of price making and of the exchanges which are only prices of one's own currency in that of some other. The price mechanism adjusts supply to demand. A rise in price is a signal to producers to produce more and to the buyers to buy less. In this way demand and supply are brought into equilibrium. So with the exchange rates, these too are only prices of pounds in terms of dollars, of dollars in terms of francs. A price does more than merely equate supply and demand in a passive way: it acts also as a kind of governor or thermostat actively adjusting one to the other. Again it is this functional relationship in contrast to the mechanical one which makes things difficult. If it were merely mechanics life would be easier and the planners might have it all their own way. All this presupposes that money is behaving itself and that the controls are not being meddled with by people who do not know what they are doing or are wilfully interfering for their own purpose.

In the early thirties for various reasons, some of which have been mentioned, the price mechanism had ceased to function properly. The exchanges were out of gear (1) because the international money had been dethroned and there was no longer an accurate way of fixing the prices of the various currencies. Once business men knew these prices. There was no getting away from the fact that the par of exchange between London and New York was $4·866 with the gold importing point at $4·90 and the exporting point at $4·83. Similarly the Paris figures were 25·225 francs with 25·34 and 25·125. Berlin was 20·43 marks with 20·53 and 20·32, but when, except for the U.S., everyone was on paper the pars disappeared and Professor Gustav Cassel invited us to contemplate the beauties of the purchasing power parities. If one were an economist such an invitation was delightful but if one were a business man with a debt to pay in New York or Paris the P.P.P. was merely a headache. No one knew what the rates of exchange were though the banks saved the situation as far as it could be saved, (2) as no one knew what the real prices were, the price mechanism as a technique for bringing supply and demand into equilibrium broke down and everything went haywire. Anything might happen to the value of a currency quite apart from fears of social legislation. Many people with money were frightened and anxious to move it to some safe centre. Speculators, using the word in the bad sense, saw excellent opportunities for easy money. The two combined caused a mass of short loan money, running into hundreds of millions, to be dumped now in this centre, now in that, causing almost complete dislocation in the exchanges. To combat the evil effects of this 'hot money' the British Government created the Exchange Equalisation Account, the object of which was to neutralise its effects. Whether the Account merely neutralised or did something more is still debated.

Abroad other developments were taking place, especially after 1931. Exchange control first developed by Germany as a protective mechanism spread rapidly until by 1932 twenty-four countries had established direct control over exchange dealings and thirty-two countries had imposed systems regulating imports by means of licence and quotas. What does exchange control aim at? It aims at just the same thing as a food control, that is, the control comes into being because there is scarcity. Butter is so short that if it is not rationed only the wealthy can have it: bread is short, but perhaps we had better not take so unfortunate an example. When there is a great scarcity some sort of control is essential. Germany began its control, because owing to reparations they never could get enough foreign exchange to pay reparations and buy the foodstuffs and raw materials they needed. Without control there would have been a wild scramble, with the inevitable breakdown. We are in a similar position today and would be in one very similar to Germany then but for the U.S. dollar loans. Shortage of exchange in reality means that a nation has more debts than credits: that its overseas accounts are not balancing. The exchanges are not the cause of the trouble but only the mirror which focuses and reflects the trouble. When, for instance, we are told that we are short of dollars and therefore cannot buy tobacco it really means that our imports are exceeding our exports. We can't have tobacco and other things because either our standard of living is too high and/or our productivity is too low.

One effect, however, of all these controls was to make trading more difficult. They were combined with much bad thinking of the mercantilist kind, that each nation should balance its accounts with every other nation. Thus bilateral agreements grew and took the place of multilateral trading. Bilateral trading suffers from the great defect that barter suffers from, what the economists call the coincidence of wants. In barter you must find, (1) a man who wants what you have got and (2) who has got what you want. So unilateral trading destroys flexibility and hinders progress. It also prevents a country buying in the cheapest market, which was considered a proper thing to do by the Victorians but is anathema to lofty idealists today. Perhaps a little moderation on both sides could solve their difficulties. It certainly strangled the world in the thirties. The more the nations practised strangulation the more it was necessary to elaborate exchange and other controls. All this and more is admirably developed by Aylmer Vallance, one of the "Nine Oxford Economists", in his chapter 'Foreign Trade and the Exchange', especially the second half.

The Germans, however, soon turned their Exchange Control under the Nazi régime into an elaborate and subtle instrument for political domination. It is all in Arndt, chapter VII. There is much more in Basch's book, *The Danube Basin and the German Economic Sphere*, but while one recommends Vallance to all, Basch is too detailed for any except advanced and enthusiastic readers. Arndt comes midway.

One might finish this rather long chapter by a word of caution on controls. It is the old, eternal and never solved problem of the individual versus the state. Freedom and order. The solution can be either a mechanical one or a spiritual one. The ideal solution will be more spiritual than mechanical and will depend upon the temper of the times. To withdraw all controls in this country at the moment would be to ask for chaos, but nevertheless controls are evils, necessary evils. How they will act will depend upon whether those operating them think them good in themselves, or necessary evils. The danger is that vested interests grow up for whom the controls are important as a livelihood. Also systems of administration petrify those who work them. It can be seen in the legal mind, the clerical mind, the academic mind and, shall we add, the civil service mind and the Trade Union mind. That's why none of these bodies should be given too much control or power. Control for control's sake is an evil. Then controls, good in themselves, can become too elaborate, too clumsy and too inept. This is patently obvious today. Finally, control enervates. The Victorians in spite of their many faults could show their present day descendants a few points. It all comes down to that elusive thing called poise.

Finally, we might notice such actions as currency devaluation and selling exchange at different rates for different purposes. These are forms of action which are only possible and indeed only necessary in highly controlled financial régimes. They aim at doing what would have been done semi-automatically and gradually in a currency based upon gold or some international currency that is keeping it in line with other currencies and the world levels of prices. The multiple exchanges, of course, are more than this and generally involve politics.

One can see how all this will affect the flow of trade and so influence production. A properly working monetary system is a *sine qua non* to a properly working industrial system and a proper relationship between the various currencies is equally necessary to international trade. It is also essential that currency manipulation, by whatsoever method, as an instrument for political or economic attack should be prevented. This can be done by the new techniques devised at or since Bretton Woods but only to the extent that currency control and reform can function. The greater setting must also be in order.

CHAPTER X

TRANSPORT

To the economist production is not complete until the commodity or article after treatment or manufacture is in the right place at the right time. Thus mutton in the refrigerators of New Zealand, wheat in Canada destined for this country, are still, from the economist's point of view, in process of production. Until they have been transported and are ready for the consumer they are not yet produced in the economic sense. Transport is therefore an extremely important factor in production, and in many cases the decisive one. The conditions and costs of transport cannot be neglected by the economic geographer but so soon as one approaches what is called the 'Economics of Transport' one discovers a subject which is exceedingly complex. Transport costs are far from being simple to calculate.

Transport may be by road, rail, river, and canal, sea and air, but in all these forms we find four factors involved, though not necessarily all in each case. They are, (1) the construction and maintenance of a prepared way, (2) the provision of terminals, (3) the provision of vessels or vehicles and (4) the supply of motive power. Thus roads are now provided free to all users by the State, while up to the present vehicles, motive power and terminals are supplied by individuals. So also with canals, though sometimes the canal company may supply the vehicles. For ocean transport and for air transport Nature supplies the way— the terminals in the form of docks, wharves or airfields, are usually supplied by corporate bodies while the vehicles are usually operated by independent companies or the State. Finally, in the case of railways, all four are supplied by the same administration, either a company or the State. Various combinations of the factors are possible, but it should be noted that in the case of railways all the services must be provided by the same body. This fact, among many, has made monopoly necessary and inevitable in their case. It is not so in the other forms of transport, though under socialism and communism it may happen. The supply of railway transport must of necessity be an expensive and elaborate undertaking as compared with that by sea, where the roadway and vehicles are supplied by others. On a sea route an individual may start with a single vessel and feel his way; for a railway an expensive track must first be constructed. So too, with road transport, but the track is supplied by the community, while the carrier supplies only the vehicle. Road transport, however, one should note is very costly to the community as a whole. This fact must be remembered when comparing railway and road costs.

Railways may be constructed for political, strategic or economic motives: all or any of these motives may be present. Thus the railways of this country were purely economic in their purpose; so too, the great lines built across the U.S.A., though no doubt political ends were served. The Canadian Pacific had a definitely political motive, though economics played a strong part. Even strategic railways may pay economically, as in India and elsewhere. But with the exception of the purely strategic railways the capital costs and running costs must be considered with care, as the cheapest railway is a very costly undertaking from all points of view, and the total expenditure has to be met from somewhere. The fact that a deficit on a national railway is made good out of taxation does not mean that the individual is not paying for it. But however carefully estimates are made, there will always be ample room for error. That is no argument against estimates being made, but perhaps it is one in favour of railway promoters being optimists. It may be necessary to build lines which will not pay at first, but which will do so ultimately, as the region is opened up. In general it is true to say that railways create their own traffic. Even when the traffic is waiting as it was in England when railway building began it will be increased through the accelerated rate of industrial growth.

When considering the railways of a country certain points should be noted:

1. Gauge: Most people take it for granted that railways will be the same gauge as at home, that is the

'standard gauge' of 4′ 8½″, but it is not necessarily so. The standard gauge is almost universal in Europe, though the Spanish is 5′ 5¾″ and that of Russia 5′ 0″. Strategic motives are responsible for these differences, though those who made the decision must have been simple-minded if they thought that engineers could not easily alter the position of a rail. In the U.S.A. they have the standard gauge. In India there are two principal gauges, the 5′ 6″ and the metre, which cause a certain amount of trouble. In Australia, New South Wales has the standard, Victoria a 5′ 8″ and the remaining States 3′ 6″. There is a great variety of gauges in Africa and S. America.

Differences in gauge matter because they prevent through traffic and make it necessary to rehandle the goods. Any 'break of gauge' is a grave evil, as handling of goods is always costly and time losing. The major reason for the different gauges has been the cost of construction. Where a community is very sparsely spread and very poor, as in say Nigeria, the problem of costs becomes almost insoluble, and so the cheaper construction is decided upon. Once, however, committed, it is difficult to change a gauge, as the Australians have found out. The Americans did so and so did we, though on a much smaller scale.

Gauge further affects the carrying capacity of a line through the size of the vehicles, though this can be rectified to a certain extent by the overhang of the wagons and carriages.

2. Alignment: this also is important. An American writer has said "The location of a railway is giving it its constitution. It may be sick, almost unto death, with accidents of construction and management but with a good constitution it will untimately recover". Alignment presents two problems which must be solved together. The line must be laid by the shortest route possible between its two terminals, but here natural features and obstacles have to be considered for cuttings, embankments, tunnels and bridges are costly, and are to be avoided as far as possible. It must go where it can obtain the maximum traffic. It is not always easy to reconcile these two demands.

3. The carrying capacity: this depends upon the gauge as we have already seen, the dimensions of the rolling stock, the

average speed of travel, which itself depends upon several factors, the terminal facilities for handling goods and turning the rolling stock round.

Finally it is as well to remember that though a railway begins as a line, it generally ends as a net-work, and it is a mistake to think of railways alone. Railways and other forms of transport are complementary as well as competitive.

There is a vast literature on transport and it is a very specialist study. All one can do here is to recommend a few introductory books and try to show how the economic geographer should approach the subject. The larger and better works come from the U.S. This is partly because the problems arising out of the rapid development of a great continent were urgent and had to be solved if the interior were to be settled and developed. Thus the great wheat-growing lands were useless without cheap transport to take the grain east. Partly because the subject appeals to the American imagination and temperament, but it is to be admitted that we British have been remarkably reluctant to write and publish. What has been the cause of this reluctance one leaves to the reader. Certain books are readable and useful for beginners.

Railways by W. V. Wood, in the Home University Library, is useful for a start, though *The Elements of Railway Economics* by Acworth is, in the writer's opinion, a clearer and better exposition. A larger and much more recent book is *Road and Rail* by Gilbert Walker. This is an excellent work, but better read after the first two. It deals with road as well as rail transport and touches upon the problems involved. Also it takes one up to the outbreak of war.

Transport interests us as geographers because it affects the total costs of production of the commodities entering into trade and through those costs their competitive ability. It must therefore have important effects upon location of industry and upon the general supply of commodities.

How much does it cost? The question is vital and would appear to be straightforward and simple. Vital it is, but certainly not simple. Let us take the case of sending butter from Hull to London. First let us enlarge the question: How much does

it cost to send butter from Hull to London? But
butter, under what conditions and how frequently? '
farmers complained that they paid more for a shor
the Danes did for a long one, and the complaint was s
correct. The railway pointed out that the Danes sh
butter in compact wooden boxes. That it came reg......, ...
in such quantities that wagons could be fully used and regular
trains made up. Further, the butter was unloaded at the
London terminal by the shippers. In contrast, the farmers'
butter came in odd lots from a few pounds to a few hundred-
weights, wrapped and packed in such a way that wagons could
not be properly loaded. The railways also handled the butter
at the terminals. There was, therefore, no comparison. It is
not a question of butter in general, but of definite amounts of
butter, under definite conditions. A great deal of bad and loose
thinking can come from asking general questions when they
should be definite and specific. Even then, the question could
not be easily answered, as was shown in the case of the Midland
farmers, who complained that Canadian cattle were being shipped
from Birkenhead to London more cheaply than their cattle.
This case brought out another vital factor. The railways
admitted the contention, but pleaded that the cattle shippers had
the alternative of sending the cattle via either Birkenhead or all
the way by sea. Which alternative they took was determined by
the total cost of shipment. The railway, therefore, was not free to
quote a price which would cover their total costs, but only such
as would give them the traffic. The price they obtained, while
not giving them a profit, at least 'cut their losses'. Further, if
they lost this traffic, the cattle would still be shipped to London,
and they having a smaller income would have to raise their
price to the Midland farmers to make up their loss of revenue.
What lies behind these arguments? The first approach to an
answer must be through an analysis of railway expenditure and
income. Acworth has useful and clear chapters on this. He
concludes that about three-fifths of the maintenance of way
expenditure is independent of the traffic passing over the lines.
Ripley in his more elaborate analysis, concludes that approximately two-thirds of the total expenditure of a railway and more

than one half of the operating expenses, are independent of the volume of traffic. The remaining one-third of all expenditures, or what amounts to the same thing, the other half of the operating expenses, is immediately responsive to any variation of business (*Transportation*, p. 55.)

It is this fact which makes the railways so urgent in their search for traffic. Their overheads are so heavy that unless an income is found they are involved immediately in grave losses. It explains why railways can pass so quickly from paying good dividends to making large deficits. Naturally when charging, the railways will wish to obtain a price which will cover total costs of transport., i.e. both fixed and moving costs, and this must be done if one considers the total volume of traffic, unless the railway is to go bankrupt or, in the case of nationalised lines, live on subsidies. It need not, however, apply and does not to individual items of traffic. Thus a railway which is not carrying its full volume of traffic (and this is by no means an easy thing to define) will take traffic at a rate below this full charge, so long as the rate charged covers the moving costs and will contribute something towards the overheads. The moving costs must be covered, otherwise the traffic will not be accepted. Anything above that, though it is not making a profit, is 'cutting its losses'; that is the overheads would still be there even if the traffic did not come: anything which helps towards these overheads is useful. Not all traffic could be carried this way, and some must be paying more than the full charges to make good the losses. It is this principle which explains the excursion train. If there are idle locomotives, idle carriages and train crews standing about, they can be employed in this manner and run at very cheap rates. The whole of the normal passenger traffic could not be so carried.

Railways, however, like all other producers, do try to systematise their charges, and have in the course of time evolved a classification of goods which is far from being simple, and which indeed is a very arbitrary affair, as it needs must be. This is correlated to a series of standard charges, which themselves have a complex background. No one would pretend that these rates aim at giving or could give a mathematically graded scale of charges. There are simple souls who desire straightforward answers to simple questions, but simplicity is not to be found in railway rating.

Mr. Gilbert Walker has some excellent chapters dealing with this subject, and they should be read. He points out that the Railway Rates Advisory Committee in 1920 estimated that there were 40 to 50 million rates in the railway companies' books, and that there is no particular reason to suppose that the number had been substantially reduced when he published his book in 1942.

The present standard charges came into force in this country in 1928 when a new classification was put into force. Goods were divided into 21 classes, which were arrived at after an elaborate survey of conditioning factors, value of the commodity, bulk, quantities offered, method of packing, risk of damage, etc. Of these factors, the value of the commodity is fundamental. This brings one to the maxim of 'Charging what the traffic will bear'. As the railways must cover their total expenses, they must find the revenue from somewhere. We have seen that certain kinds of goods cannot pay much if they are to move at all. Thus road metal which must move in great quantities cannot pay a high rate. It is put in No. 3. The highest grade, No. 21, deals with gold and silver and manufactures thereof. When one first reads the classification it seems to be completely arbitrary and almost fantastic. Thus No. 19 includes among other things, leather goods, hobby horses, soldiers' busbies, boilers and water heaters. No. 13, wooden balls for throwing at coco-nuts, cockles, window frames and raw cotton. But there is much method in the apparent madness, even though it looks as if the compilers were surrealists. The Act of 1921 which set out the principles of classification, in addition to such things as value, bulk, risk of damage, cost of handling, includes 'all relevant circumstances' and also the saving of cost when traffic is offered in large consignments. None of these conditions were new to the railways which had, by force of circumstances, been forced to take them into consideration. Of these factors the most important is the value of the goods as this sets the limit to the possible charge. 'Charging what the traffic will bear' is not a technique confined only to railways. The Eastern trader employs it always, and it is usual among doctors. Applied within reasonable limits it is good and proper, but it can be and has been gravely abused at times.

Distance must next be considered. It was early found that standard charges could not be the same throughout a long route, and the practice of tapering rates was gradually evolved. Detail of the present system for this country can be seen in *Road and Rail* p. 52. On the Continent different solutions have been tried out, but it is in the U.S.A. with its great distances from which the best examples can be drawn, and the reader is referred to Locklin: *Economics of Transport*. There is no simple solution to this very complex problem, and Locklin sums the matter up very well when he writes, "The rate of progression of distant scales is a matter which calls for the exercise of judgment. It depends in large measure upon the revenue needs of the carriers and the ability of traffic to move under high rates. In constructing rate scales, the Interstate Commerce Commission has relied less upon theoretical calculations than upon the necessity of fitting the scale into existing rate levels and joining them to rate structures in bordering territories" (p. 182).

Ripley has pointed out that railway competition is of three distinct types:

> Competition of routes.
> Competition of facilities.
> Competition of markets.

It is the first and the third which interest the geographer as such, for it is through this competition that what I call distance distortion takes place. If this be true of railways, it is even more so of all transport, though for the sake of simplicity we will confine ourselves to the railways. Rival lines compete with each other for traffic between terminals which they both serve. The routes may be practically parallel, as in this country before the railway amalgamations which took place between the two wars, or they may diverge to such an extent that they serve entirely different communities except at the terminals. The best examples of this are found in the U.S.A., because of its great size, and the examples quoted are those given by Ripley in his *Railroads:*

"Recent instances of wasteful and circuitous all-rail transportation are abundant. A few typical ones will suffice to show how common the evil is. President Ramsay of the Wabash has testified as to the roundabout competition with the Pennsylvania Railroad between Philadelphia and Pittsburg by which sometimes as much as fifty-seven per cent of traffic between those two points may be diverted from the direct route. 'They haul freight 700 miles around sometimes to meet a point in competition 200 miles away.' Chicago and New Orleans are 912 miles apart, and about equally distant—2,500 miles—from San Francisco. The traffic manager of the Illinois Central states that company 'engages in San Francisco business directly via New Orleans from the Chicago territory, and there is a large amount of that business, and we engage in it right along.' Wool from Idaho and Wyoming may move west 800 miles, to San Francisco; and thence via New Orleans over the Southern Pacific route to Boston. This case, therefore, represents a superfluous lateral haul of nearly a thousand miles between two points nearly 2,500 miles apart. The Canadian Pacific used to take business for San Francisco, all rail, from points as far south as Tennessee and Arkansas, diverting it from the direct way via Kansas City."

Such competition may have marked effects upon the location of industry. It has been said that the rise of Birkenhead as a milling town was partly due to the rate wars between the U.S. trunk and Gulf lines affecting the cost of wheat and flour at various points in the U.S. and at Birkenhead. But it is a complicated business to unravel, as will be seen if one cares to look into the case in Ripley's *Railway Problems.*

Competition of facilities need not detain us here, and we will pass to the third form of competition, that of markets. Here the railways are no longer the principals, but only the agents, though their influence can be very powerful. Competition of markets is the competition between rival producing centres to sell their goods in a common market.

We have seen already that production includes both form and place utilities. Transport creates the latter, and the costs are often much more elastic than the factory costs. Hence producers will do their utmost to obtain concessions in freight charges in order to reduce their total costs. Under ideal conditions, those producing centres, other things being equal, ought to supply the markets nearest to them, i.e. distance ought to be a geographical control affecting location of industry. But where the railways are competing with each other for traffic, each company will be anxious to keep producers within its region in business. Where a producer cannot compete because his total costs—factory and transport—are too high, he will approach the railway for a reduced charge. Where the railway is not operating to full capacity it will be tempted to accede for, it will be argued, if the company goes out of production, the railway loses all the traffic and income. A lower rate will keep the company in production and, while not paying total costs of transport to the railway, will at least enable it to cut its losses. Sherrington writes, "How is one to draw a line between the following cases: that of raw material carried at a loss to a works, the product of which can pay sufficient railway charges to offset the earlier deficit, the fabrication of the product moreover, requiring movement of fuel to the works being carried at a profit; and that of traffic carried wholly at a loss, yet offset by the surplus profits derived from some other traffic?" (p. 94). How indeed, save by a wide experience backed by a sense of fair play and balanced judgment. The official, whether of an independent company or a State owned and managed railway, must have very considerable freedom and must not be tied by either red tape or shallow ideas of equalitarian justice.

It is not one's intention to write a précis on the economics of transport, and the reader is referred to the various writers already quoted. What has been said is for the purpose of drawing the reader's attention to the immense complexity of the price-making business in transport. Theoretically, a perfect system of charging ought to leave the suppliers of transport in a neutral position, so that the location of an industry would depend upon such factors as nearness to raw materials and markets, to efficiency of management and various other factors. That, however, does not imply any simple system of charging. Distance distortion must be allowed for in any normal localisation.

So far one has assumed that the railways are managed with average ability and with honesty. It is impossible to conduct operations on such a vast and varied scale without anomalies appearing. That, of course, is the reason for such a body as the Railway Tribunal and Advisory Committees. Where railways are competing as independent systems, or where water transport cuts in, then distortion must appear. To what extent will depend upon the experience and good sense of the competitors. Railways may, however, be used as instruments for industrial development and national policy by Governments. This will cause very considerable distortion. The major problems of distortion, which are both frequent and marked, arise between national systems where national economic policies are being enforced. Competition between competing companies within the same country can, and in the past did, cause a great deal of special rate making and discrimination. This was most marked in the U.S.A., but was by no means confined to that country. It was gradually eliminated by amalgamation or suppressed by law. Many of the outstanding cases of the past are well worth reading, as illustrating principles involved. The Americans are better documented in these than we. Ripley's *Problems* is still well worth looking at. But if the reader wishes to get a view of the problem in its immensity and intricacy, let him turn to *International Rail Transport* by Sir Ralph L. Wedgewood. I do not recommend the book as light reading, nor to the beginner, except for a casual turning over of the pages. It will endorse what has been said already. Railway organisation is no simple thing.

So far one has discussed only railway problems, and must now turn to sea transport. We have seen already that one great distinguishing feature between the two is that all the factors necessary for transport must be supplied by the railways themselves, while such is not the case for sea transport. Nature provides the way while, ordinarily, the terminals are supplied by other bodies than those who supply the vehicles. As result, competition can insinuate itself more readily. There is however, a further factor of vital difference. The ocean and seas are free to all comers of whatever nationality. One hardly expects to see Dutch locomotives and trains running on British lines in competition with our own. Railway traffic in so far as it is national, is largely a protected industry. Its problems are internal, and up to a point can be settled internally, though not quite. Coasting steamers may compete and do though only to a limited extent. In the U.S.A. the sea transport from the West Coast via the Panama competes with the transcontinental lines.

On the seas all nations can compete. Here Dutch vessels can and do compete with ours. This competition may be modified by Navigation Laws, but there are strict limits to such interferences, as we found out long ago. It is quite easy to lay down the law that British goods must be carried only in British ships, but it is equally easy for Americans, French, Germans, and all the world to legislate in a similar way for their nationals, so that the ships never obtain a return cargo. This business of return freights is of vital importance if sea transport is to be cheap. The loss of the British export trade in coal is not only a matter of the price of the coal, but of ships compelled to sail in ballast as we import in bulk a vast amount more than we export. In the old days, ships filled up with coal at cheap rates. Even if they did not make a profit, they cut their losses. Sea-water is never cheap to carry. The writer can remember when sailing to India in a cargo vessel loaded with rails, which are heavy in comparison to the space they take up, the ship called at Naples and loaded 1,000 tons of potatoes for Bombay. The freight was £1 a ton. The company made an additional £1,000 towards expenses. The Italians sold their potatoes, while the Indians got some extra food at an extra cost of 1/10d. per pound. That would not be possible if Italian potatoes had to be carried in Italian ships. Nothing can be more detrimental to international trade than protection of national shipping. This country in particular is interested in freedom of shipping, as it is, or was, a major export.

In the 19th century, shipping was essentially an economic

and commercial affair, but during this century politics and war
have more and more taken a part, so that it is difficult to dissect
one from the other.   Mance in *International Sea Transport*
has a chapter on 'Political and Economic Factors' which is well
worth reading, as is the whole book.   Perhaps, however, one
is proceeding too quickly.   If it was difficult to recommend
books on railway problems, it is more so in the present case.
A good book to start on is Hardy's *Seaways and Sea Trade*.   It
is relatively recent if one excludes the late war, and is fairly comprehensive.   An older book which is still worth while for
certain chapters is Kirkcaldy's *British Shipping*.   This was published in 1919.   Book I, the *Evolution of the Ship*, is useful for those
who have not been born and bred in seaports and even for some
who have.   Book III, *Trade Routes*, is also useful.   There is an
excellent chapter, 'Twenty-four Trading Voyages', which helps
one to visualise the tramp steamer at work.   It is not as out of date
as might appear.   There are chapters on the Suez and Panama
Canals, but for these one should be aware of Siegfried's *Suez
and Panama*.   This is a middle-brow book of some length, but
like all Siegfried's books, very interesting.   Siegfried has the
art of making things interesting, and is none the worse for that.
He gives the whole story of both canals, which can be read
in bed when the day is done.   But he has also excellent little
diagrams, showing the zones served by both canals.   When
talking of ship canals it is well to remember that the Suez and
Panama are not the only ones.   Actually, the Sault Ste Marie
Canal has the largest tonnage passing through—nearly twice
that of these other two put together.   Beware of looking only
at the spectacular.

Sargent's *Seaways of the Empire* is more severe reading.   He
has an interesting discussion in his first chapter on what is meant
by tonnage and its relation to carrying capacity.   This is very
vital to all proper thinking and discussion.   Tonnage is about
as illuminating to the uninitiated as horse power, and what
that means even the engineers don't seem able to say, at least to
me. Mance has a useful paragraph 'Tonnage Measurement' in the
above mentioned book :

G

"The gross tonnage of a ship is the sum in cubic feet of all the various enclosed spaces of a vessel divided by 100. The net tonnage is the gross tonnage less certain deductions on account of crew spaces, engine-room, water-ballast and other spaces not used for passengers or cargo. The dead-weight tonnage or carrying capacity is the number of tons (of 2,240 lbs.) of cargo, passengers, fuel and stores that a vessel is capable of carrying when charged to the load line. Displacement tonnage is the weight of the vessel and contents in tons when charged to the load line in sea water. It is evident that gross tonnage is always greater than net tonnage. As a general rule, for merchant vessels of ordinary type the deadweight carrying capacity is always greater than the net tonnage and is usually greater than the gross tonnage. As an example, a cargo steamer with a nominal deadweight tonnage of about 8,000 tons of cargo, fuel and stores will have a displacement of about 11,500 tons, a gross tonnage of about 5,200 and a net tonnage of about 3,200. In principle harbour and canal dues have been levied on the net tonnage of vessels, which is supposed to represent the earning capacity of the ship."

Here is plenty of room for misunderstanding, not only on the readers' part, but also between nations. As Mance says: "The measurement of tonnage is of importance, since the tonnage determines the amount of the dues charged by port and harbour authorities, lighting authorities and the Suez and Panama Canals. Unless the measurements apply equally to ships of all nations, some will benefit by smaller charges. The case of the *Leviathan* is quoted as an (extreme) example. When taken over by the U.S.A. her tonnage was given as 23,500 net. In the U.S. this was reassessed at 27,696, but later remeasurement made it 15,800. The League of Nations undertook the task of drawing up a uniform system, though it has not been adopted. The rules are highly technical and comprise 92 articles, several mathematical tables and 120 figures. So we landsmen must beware when we read shipping statistics.

Competition for freights is keen, even when there is no political interference. What it costs to run a ship will depend upon many factors such as the cost of labour, and this depends upon the rates of pay and conditions of living in the ship; upon the conditions of loading; conditions of repair and sea-worthiness of the ships. If these costs are high, because high standards are demanded, while abroad standards are low, it may mean the loss of the trade. Such questions and problems are discussed in Mance's *International Sea Transport* in chapters III, 'Technical and Safety Questions', and IV, 'Labour'. Such discussions may not seem, at first sight, of importance to the economic geographer, but anything which affects price and costs, matters. Differences in costs due to the above factors may not matter much when the competition is between peoples living on the same relative plane, for the differences will be slight and can be adjusted. Where, however, the planes are very different as, say, between ourselves and the Japanese, adjustment may well be impossible, and if so, annihilation follows. The Lancashire operatives found that out between the two wars. Protection is impossible where trade is international. Lancashire could not be protected, and indeed it was the protection of the 'sheltered' industries which helped to annihilate Lancashire. So with international shipping. One nation cannot insist upon high and costly conditions for shipping if others do not, unless efficiency is equally high to maintain it.

Mance discusses these political and economic factors in a separate chapter, which should be read. It is very clear and straight reading. First it gives a résumé of the general shipping position between the two wars, and then the policies of the principal maritime countries. Such detail as is given is often more than the reader requires, but should be read 'to be for-gotten'. Having read it, even when forgotten, one is aware that the problem is complex. The danger of books on economic geography is that we are compelled to simplify too much and to make sweeping generalisations, which can be dangerous if the background against which they are made is not known. As has been said already little books are excellent to read when one has read the larger ones. When reading the paragraph on Japan, one should note Sir George Sanson's remark that the

Japanese progress in shipping was more due 'to the character and mentality of the Japanese people' than to what the Government had done. They had a "determination to succeed: enquiring and adaptive minds; energy, a capacity for organisation down to the smallest detail and for hard work on the basis of a simple and relatively inexpensive standard of living". Something which the Victorians possessed and which this generation has lost. The whole chapter is vastly important.

Nothing will be said here about air-transport partly because space forbids and partly because air-transport is still in the experimental stage, not only on its mechanical and engineering side but also in its business organisation and administration. Further, more than any other form of transport it has got mixed up with war and politics so that any discussion is more politics than economics. For those who wish, however, there are certain books such as *International Air Transport*, by Mance and Wheeler, and *Air Transportation* by Claude E. Puffer. One day air-transport will come to its own and revolutionise certain aspects of travel and freight conveyance but that day has not yet arrived.

CHAPTER XI

FOREIGN TRADE AND ITS RELATION
TO HOME TRADE

GOODS when made must pass from the producers to the consumers as all production is for consumption. This business of transferring goods is called trade or commerce. It may be on a very small and local scale as when a village smallholder sells food to a fellow villager or the butcher sells locally bred and killed meat. It may be on a world scale as when Egyptian cotton or Brazilian coffee are exported to consumers scattered in every continent. Between these two extremes there will be found every degree of magnitude and of complexity. Trade is inevitable if men are to live decent and civilised lives, for two obvious reasons. Modern man wants a great range of things which cannot be supplied locally or even nationally, and further, no one man can make the variety of goods which he desires to consume. Simple economics are only possible if life is equally simple and austere. If too simple it becomes brutish. Plain living and high thinking do not go together after a point.

The trade then of a given country will equal all the transactions which take place. This we are unable to calculate not so much for statistical reasons as because of the cost in time and money. Statistics are extremely expensive to collect and produce. Like every other desirable thing one has to strike a balance. The internal trade can, however, be partly estimated by taking production figures. That is why agricultural, mining and industrial figures are so useful. The first two are easier to obtain than the last though now with the industrial census a big gap has been filled in. It takes a considerable time, however, to get the data worked out and published.

All these transactions imply traders, and that brings us to the business of marketing and how it is done. People are often astonished at the difference between the price which the producer obtains and the price the consumer pays. Yet it is interesting to note how few producers attempt to market their own produce. When they do one remarks that their selling price is seldom less than that of the trader and in any case not much, nor does the producer seem to make a much greater net profit as he had hoped. The selling prices in the market places are very much the same as in the shops: the same is true of the itinerant salesman. The old economics' premise of free competition argued that the service of the trader could not be overpaid as high prices would attract competitors and so prices would fall again and vice versa. Such an argument is perfectly correct if the premise of free competition holds and is quite valid as a starting point but too often this was forgotten. Today we talk in terms of imperfect competition and monopoly. A good book on *Monopoly* is that by E. A. G. Robinson. We all know in fact that everywhere there were frictions, even before the first war, which could make unreasonable and unjust gaps between the producer's and consumer's prices. None the less marketing is an intricate difficult and costly business. That it needs examination from time to time there is no doubt. After the Great War the Ministry of Agriculture and Fisheries issued a long series of books on marketing, some 26 in all, which went into considerable detail. Thus the "Report on the Marketing of Cattle and Beef in England and Wales" No. 20 covers 170 pages. The veal trade and trade in hides and skins were subject to separate reports as were also the trade in refrigerated beef, mutton and lamb. You see it was and is an elaborate affair. When one had read all these reports— they were by no means exhaustive though slightly exhausting— one realised what an exciting thing a mutton chop might be and what a vast number of people had handled it before it arrived on one's plate. Could one have had all these handling costs worked out to the fifth or tenth decimal place one would then have been ready, after eating the chop, to talk of marketing reform. So with Covent Garden. What a chaos both physically and commercially. Yet when the planners step in one does not often see the price go down or the producers more satisfied. That is no argument against the most careful scrutiny and need for improvement. It only points to the wickedness of human

nature. *Caveat emptor*, let the buyer beware. In India one way
of insulting a man—there are many—is to call him a 'bania'.
It would have been positively dangerous to call a sepoy one.
Yet when translated it means more or less a dealer in grain, a
grocer, a shopkeeper. The implication was that a 'bania' was
always a cheat, a liar, one who gives false weight and value—
and he generally was and did. Who would say that really high
standards of dealing are usual in the West? Reform must always
be based upon a realistic view of human nature. Few men will
work for love and few men are really honest: most men are
corruptible directly or indirectly. The writer was once a quartermaster, and by the time he had finished had a qualified view of
mankind! All plans for marketing improvement must include
moral education as well as 'planning' as understood. Part of
the planning, however, should allow for human cupidity for if
suppressed in one direction it will come out in another—witness
the black market. Read Lord Keynes' *The General Theory of
Employment*, chapter 24. It is full of distilled wisdom and Keynes
could be very wise. Read especially the paragraph on page 374:

"For my own part, I believe that there is social and psychological justification for significant inequalities of incomes and
wealth, but not for such large disparities as exist today.
There are valuable human activities which require the motive
of money-making and the environment of private wealth-
ownership for their full fruition. Moreover, dangerous
human proclivities can be canalised into comparatively
harmless channels by private wealth, which, if they cannot
be satisfied in this way, may find their outlet in cruelty, the
reckless pursuit of personal power and authority, and other
forms of self-aggrandisement. It is better that a man should
tyrannise over his bank balance than over his fellow-citizens;
and whilst the former is sometimes denounced as being but
a means to the latter, sometimes at least it is an alternative.
But it is not necessary for the stimulation of these activities
and the satisfaction of these proclivities that the game should
be played for such high stakes as at present. Much lower
stakes will serve the purpose equally well, as soon as the

players are accustomed to them.   The task of transmuting
human nature must not be confused with the task of manag-
ing it.   Though in the ideal commonwealth men may have
been taught or inspired or bred to take no interest in the
stakes, it may still be wise and prudent statesmanship to allow
the game to be played, subject to rules and limitations, so
long as the average man, or even a significant section of the
community, is in fact strongly addicted to the money-
making passion."

Marketing includes not only the great wholesale markets but
the innumerable local ones and finally all the shops of which
the number in this country is variously estimated from 750,000
to 1,000,000.   Could we handle this vast and diversified wholesale and retail trade better and more cheaply?   This is not quite
our subject so we must leave it, but for the inquisitive certain
books might be mentioned.   *The Shops of Britain* by Levy, published by Kegan Paul, 1947, chapters 1, 2, and 12 will help to
answer the above question.   Levy quotes from another writer,
'Amalgamations remove the shopkeeper but seldom the shop'.
An interesting remark worth chewing over, but a woman with
three or four children and no help will find the answer to it
much more quickly than a male student in economics or perhaps
even some of the female ones.   *Retail Distribution* by Henry
Smith and the Oxford Press is recommended for chapter 2 which
has useful charts and tables.   Another of Levy's, *Retail Trade
Associations*, 1942, chapter 19.   He quotes from Macmillan,
Middle Way, p. 207: ". . . Can we find some method of industrial
reorganisation which will enable us to abandon *laissez-faire*,
which is 'ruinous in one way' without leaving ourselves at the
mercy of 'private monopoly' which 'is ruinous in another' ? "
A difficult question to answer.

Finding the volume of internal or home trade is then a most
difficult business and can only be done by using all kinds of
statistics which can never be added together in a simple answer.
The London and Cambridge Economics Services Bulletin II, Volume
26, May 1948, has an interesting series of tables headed 'Annual
Statistics' which gives outputs for the main British Industries.

The August number has two articles: 'Index of Industrial Production' by C. F. Carter: and 'Index of Internal Activity' which is in percentages of 1942. The former is a corrected version of a new series begun in the May number. As is remarked we shall have to wait for the forthcoming census of production.

If it is difficult to obtain national figures, world figures are still more elusive. Attempts have been made and the results can be seen in *Industrialisation and Foreign Trade*, League of Nations, 1945. An excellent study but definitely not recommended to the beginner: more advanced students should certainly look at it. It contains an Annex, 'Indices of Manufacturing, 1870–1938. Here are two sets of tables, one with 1913 and the other with 1925–29 as the base. Taking Table No. 1 for what it is worth one can see a ninefold increase in world manufacture—22·4 to 185·0. The figures for the U.S. and Germany are of roughly the same (11 and 7 fold respectively) order but for the U.K. is about $2\frac{1}{2}$ fold. Russia is more spectacular—41 fold. Japan is about 35 fold. This would account for the vast increase in world trade between 1870 and 1939 but one must be cautious. It is most dangerous to take these figures without first reading the preliminary warnings on pp. 123–9. Then as an afterthought there are, 'Notes Concerning the Computation of the National Indices,' pp. 144–53. Further, these figures are percentages of a given base. One must know what that base is. For instance of two countries, A, shall we say, has a coal output of 200,000,000 tons at a given date: B has 1,000,000. A increases its output by 50,000,000 tons, i.e. 25%: B increases output to 7,000,000 tons, i.e. 700%. It would appear that A is a stagnant moribund affair compared with the spectacular B. If, further, both countries have roughly the same population the material condition of the two countries will not stand comparison. Beware of percentage increases when one does not know the base figures. The author tried during the war to get some idea of the real increase in Indian war manufacture and was supplied with percentages—naturally for security reasons. Actually one knows that the war production was slight compared with the massive figures of this country. It is, however, all rather difficult for the beginner and if not statistically minded a

G*

little repulsive. For those who are used to statistics such references are recommended.

We turn now to foreign trade which is more attractive to students of economic geography, partly because the figures are much more available and partly to us islanders because such trade is vital to our existence, and by vital one literally means that it is a matter of life and death or at least life and a potato existence. With the Americans foreign trade is vastly important, and any sudden cessation would cause an economic crisis of the first magnitude. Nevertheless given time the U.S. could readapt itself and live at pretty much the same high standards. The immediate problems would be great gluts of foodstuffs and even of certain types of manufactures. True they would have to go short of coffee, and for that there is no substitute: they would be short of sugar for a time, but that could be quickly rectified by substituting beet for cane. Silk would be cut off to the grief and suffering of many of the female members of the nation, but they could console themselves with artificial silk, though after all silk is silk and rayon is rayon. There are such who do not readily know the difference, males rather than females, but then there are those who do not readily know the difference between butter and margarine. One hardly knows whether to pity or envy them. With us, however, a total cessation of trade would not be a question of getting rid of gluts of food, of finding a substitute for coffee or tea nor of silk stockings. Our problem would be one of complete lacks. It is a curious thing that the mass of British people still fail to realise it. Only the Germans fully appreciated it, and would have taught us to do so but for American help.

Foreign trade must always be considered with reference to total trade and production, otherwise it leads to distortion and very bad thinking. What then is the relative importance of one to the other? The first Census of Production in 190 put the proportion of industrial production for export at on third. Professor Clay asserts[1] that by 1912 it was probabl higher. In 1924 it was 27%: in 1930 only 22%. Clay est

[1] "Place of Exports in British Industry after the War", *Econ. Journ.* June–Sept. 1942.

mates it was 17% in 1935 and 15% in 1938. One might hazard a guess that it is round about 25% today. The position of the United Kingdom was and is unique. Perhaps Belgium ran us fairly close. Most other countries devoted a much smaller percentage of their energies to external trade. The highest percentage figure reached for the U.S. was 16% in 1919 but it fell away and by 1939 was 7·6%: in 1943 it had risen to 11·0%. Today it is probably little more as their increase in exports is fully matched by the increased productivity of industry. The figures can be seen in the *Statistical Abstract for the U.S. 1947*, p. 889, table 994. It is doubtful if at any time the figure exceeded 16% for Germans or 10% for France. If one reverses the figures the dominant position of the home trade stands out at once—66% for the U.K. rising to say 75% today, 89% for the U.S.: 84% Germany: 90% France. These are estimates, but they illustrate the dominance of the home to foreign trade. It would seem then that for many countries foreign trade is not so very important, though one could hardly say that of our own country. Such a deduction would be wrong in all cases. The importance of foreign trade can not be measured by these percentages. It is like a key industry, the value of the total output may be small but vital to some larger industrial output: like those curious traces of minerals in the blood which once were thought to be merely impurities, but which, when lacking cause unpleasant things to happen to one. The story of the devil and the golfer is based upon this fact. How vital, however, will depend upon many factors. It will depend in the case of imports upon relative and absolute lacks. Thus we in this country could not carry on any of our textile industries except the woollen and that to only 1/3 its activity, and a little linen without imports. Except for iron ore, and not all of that is home produced, we must import all our metals; all our oils, mineral and vegetable. So with foodstuffs. We could not and can not feed ourselves. Today we are realising this though dimly. Had it not been for the American and Dominion loans and the money from the sale of the Argentine railways we would have known clearly.

If one takes the case of France, foreign trade is not equally

vital.   Before the war the French could feed themselves from
their own agriculture, in an average year up to about 90% of
total consumption.   In a bad year 80% and in a very good year
100%.   That, remember, when all could eat what they wished,
and the French were the best fed nation in Europe.   There are
two ways of balancing demand and supply.   The positive one of
producing so much that all can have as much as they desire;
the negative when demand is made to fit the supply, when you
eat what you get.   The French food supplies were almost adequate on the positive side.   The position was and is not so good
as regards raw materials for manufacture.   Like us they depend
upon imported fibres, minerals and metals, except iron ore and
bauxite.   Their problem for the future is in this respect much
simpler than ours.   Given sense and organisation, the French
can reach a balance of trade again in a few years.   Neither did
their textile industries depend upon the export market as much as
ours, except silk.   Foreign trade France must have, but its
problem is not as grave as ours.

The U.S. as one has said already depends on foreign trade
for its prosperity even less, but a cessation in the import of many
raw materials especially the rarer and alloy metals would hold up
a host of activities.   Within twenty years, however, they could
readjust themselves for most things, though given the present
patterns of industry and consumption foreign trade is vastly
important.   One cannot interfere with an established pattern
of foreign trade without affecting the internal pattern of total
industrial activity.

So far one has been talking of foreign trade as if it affected a
nation's industrial activities equally, but this is not so.   Certain
industries are intimately connected with foreign trade while
others are hardly touched.   The position of Great Britain before
1914 was rather remarkable.   As Clay in the above mentioned
article writes, "The country had too many eggs in too few
baskets: cotton manufacturers accounted for a third, coal and
steel for a fifth of the total exports.   The United Kingdom was
providing 70% of the total world's exports of cotton manufactures, 80% of the world's coal exports, and practically the
whole of the world's export of ships."   The whole article is

well worth reading.   One can see how the pattern of our industrial development was conditioned by all this.   We Lancashire
men were born and reared on the tacit understanding that the
world would buy our cottons.   The well-being of hundreds of
thousands depended upon this assumption.   The same is true
of the great shipbuilding centres and of the miners.   Marriages
may be made in heaven and babies brought in the doctor's hand-
bag, but when the industrial production and the export curves
are correlated with the marriage and birth rates, they show a
remarkable coincidence.   The fact is that the British population
has been born, grown in numbers and lived at its various standards on the tacit understanding that the world would take our
manufactures and supply us with raw materials.   This vital
fact was never appreciated by the British people even between the
wars when they were not keeping themselves by their own work,
for the difference was made up by their grandfathers' savings.
It is not appreciated even now because they are still making up
the difference by the same rake's progress, witness the sale of the
Argentine railways, and by the contracting of loans which they
have as much hope or intention of repaying as had Micawber
his.

A sudden change in foreign demands may therefore have quite
grave and even disastrous results upon home employment and
the nature of that employment.   This is true of all countries
but the more a country is involved in foreign trade the less it is
master in its own house.   Lancashire found that out when
masters and men were disputing over the number of looms an
operative should manage.   They thought of it, at least the men
did, as if it were a private Lancashire affair.   Actually it was
settled by the Japanese women in the Japanese mills and the
Lancashire operatives ended by tending no looms at all.   The
policy of full employment depends upon this intimate and delicate relationship, a fact not in the least realised by most people
in this country though Sir Stafford Cripps has recently hinted it.
More will be said of full employment later.

Let us now turn to world trade, a rather ambitious thing to do
in so small a book.   Most of what will be said is taken from two
League of Nations publications, *The Network of World Trade*

and *Europe's Trade*. A third might be added, *Industrialisation and Foreign Trade*. Taken together these fill some 432 pages which may appear somewhat formidable, but if the reader fears so great a task let him read the 'Summary of Results' pp. 7–10 and the Introduction, pp. 7–8 of the first two. Some will then be tempted to look further where they will find a great number of most useful tables. These are the figures from which so much of the present-day discussion starts. There are, first, five pages of definitions. One might read particularly the note on the 'Unit of currency' as the figures are given in dollars. Now one of the last hopes of those clutching at stability in trade figures is the dollar, but even a dollar isn't what it was, not even the gold dollar. "Values are shown in dollars of the 1934 parity, that is, one dollar equalling 0·88867 gramme of fine gold. For 1928, however, two sets of figures are shown, one representing dollars at the old parity (one dollar equalling 1·50463 gramme of fine gold), and the other dollars at the 1934 parity (new gold dollar)." Alas and alack, what a contrast to the British sovereign which consisted of 123·27447 grains of gold 11/12 fine which never faltered but died at its post without losing weight. Perhaps that was why it died. Its ghost, the paper pound, like all wraiths varies in density from time to time. The table below gives a summary of world trade.

Again may I remind the reader who will be tired of so many reminders that such a table should not be overworked. It is too simplified and condensed. The world cannot be put into a small table like this. That, of course, is why this 'Network' is so long as it is amplifying the table but reminders are necessary.

The table is worth a slight discussion, but this might be prefaced by an interesting statement. "Roughly, the value of goods which countries used to exchange correspond to a third of the United States national income. During the few years preceding the present war (1942), it was about the same magnitude as the national income of the United Kingdom or Germany." That puts it in its proper perspective. Foreign trade is a 'key industry' unlocking the door to world industry or, shall we say, a master key unlocking a great number of doors into industrial rooms of various sizes.

TABLE I

WORLD TRADE IN MERCHANDISE, SUMMARY TABLE.

Adjusted dollar figures.   "Frontier values."

	Imports				Exports			
	1928	1935	1937	1938	1928	1935	1937	1938
Values in terms of								
old $ gold (000,000's)	35,482	12,427	16,638	14,518	32,615	11,236	15,006	12,944
new $ gold (000,000's)	60,080	21,042	28,171	24,583	55,223	19,025	25,409	21,917
$ (000,000's)	35,482	21,042	28,171	24,583	32,615	19,025	25,409	21,917
£ sterling (000,000's)[a]	7,291	4,271	5,695	5,027	6,702	3,861	5,137	4,482
Percentage movement of *values* (1928 = 100) in terms of:								
gold............	100	35·0	46·9	40·9	100	34·4	46·0	39·7
$	100	59·3	79·4	69·3	100	58·3	77·9	67·2
£ sterling	100	58·6	78·1	68·9	100	57·6	76·7	66·9
Percentage movement of *prices* (1928 = 100) in terms of:								
gold............	100	41	47	44·5	100	40·5	46	43·5
$	100	70	79·5	75·5	100	68·5	78	74
£ sterling	100	69	78	75	100	68	76·5	73·5
Percentage movement of *quantum* (1928 = 100)	100	85	100	91·5	100	85	100	91

[a] The exchange value of the £ sterling was, in 1928, $4·8667 (new $ gold 8·2403); in 1935, $4·9272; in 1937, $4·9462; and in 1938 $4·8903.

[1] It would fall outside the scope of this volume to enter into details of the changes in the prices and quantum of trade which have been described at some length in the successive issues of the *Review of World Trade*.

From *The Network of World Trade*, p. 16.

Note now that the volume of world trade differs greatly according to which dollar you select, the old or the new.   Then notice the third line of figures which would be the one produced in the Statistical Abstracts and by those who copy therefrom.   The 1928 figure is the 'old' dollar, while that for 1935 is the 'new' dollar. The Abstracts will not warn you. The fourth line in Sterling depends upon the value of the dollar. As the 1935 dollar is less valuable in terms of pounds the sterling value of the trade is not of the same order as for 1928. For comparison's sake, you can either choose the old gold value or the new, but you can't take both as in lines 3 and 4 without falling into grave error. Note again how the trade fell as between 1928 and 1935 and how little it had risen even by 1938. Then turn to the last line—the quantum of trade. In 1928 it was 100: in 1935, 85 and in 1938, 91·5. That is, the dollar figures exaggerate the fall in real trade. Dollar or sterling values fell but the actual commodities fell much less. They point out all these facts in the text which accompanies the table and others too, so that a careful and honest reader cannot make a mistake though tables are too often torn from their context. Two things are necessary in all this work. First to be honest and that means that one must put aside one's political bias. You can't be honest in economic thinking if you start as so many people do by announcing that they are prepared to consider a question with a perfectly open mind, 'but remember I'm a conservative or labour'. That should be left to the politicians who mostly believe that truth is relative. Scientists must search for the truth. That is the second need. Careful search. Truth rarely reveals herself gratis. Like Jacob working for Rachel you must work for seven years and even then an unscrupulous Laban may palm off on you Leah, who may be tender-eyed, a doubtful expression, but still is not Rachel. Maybe like Jacob you will serve another seven years and then indeed you are a scientist if it can be said of you as of Jacob, 'they seemed unto him but a few days, for the love he had to her'. What a love story and yet people won't read the Bible which is the wisest and most human book in the world!

This table has suggested a series of warnings which might be tabulated for further use.

1. How exactly is the particular table compiled? The wider the scope, the more complex the data. World figures must always be compiled with scrupulous care and never

used unless one knows their limitations. Always be on
your guard with world figures.

2. If in money what exactly was the purchasing power of the
unit used and to what degree was it subject to fluctuation?
The above mentioned change in the value of the dollar is
only what happens to any unit of value. All currencies
fluctuate greatly and so ought to be corrected by the appro-
priate index numbers.

3. Money values are never adequate. It is quite impossible
to get any real view unless one comes to physical quantities.
The 'quantum' figures try to do this. But they too are full
of pitfalls. It is relatively easy to compile figures of raw
materials or rather it appears to be so. Actually it is not.
Tons of coal, though you must distinguish between long
tons, short tons, and metric tons: bales of cotton which
may be of 400, 740, 250, 510, 440 lbs: barrels of oil which
also vary. Still these can be reduced to some common
figure. It is not so much the physical measurement as the
qualitative. Coal, cotton, oil differ greatly in qualities.
If it is not too easy to get accurate figures in raw materials
it is infinitely more difficult in the case of manufactured
articles. The tables become more and more elaborate.
So when we come to a summation of all these quantities
and qualities both raw and manufactured the 'quantum'
is a very complex and delicate idea. The statistical
techniques for doing this are complex and hedged around
with a mass of qualifications.

Turn now to the composition of the trade. Again the
warnings, "Any distribution of trade according to a restricted
number of categories must fail to reflect the complexity of international trade, composed as it is of thousands of articles representing different stages of manufacture. The line of demarcation between raw materials and manufactured goods is naturally
arbitrary—yarn, for example, is included among manufactured
goods but refined mineral oils among raw materials. Under
foodstuffs are included, besides raw articles of foods, factory
produced goods such as refined sugar and canned meats, and also

vegetable fatty oils, in spite of the fact that such oils are also used for technical purposes." The classification followed is the Brussels Classification into: (1) Foodstuffs and live animals; (2) Materials, raw or partly manufactured; (3) Manufactured articles.

COMPOSITION OF WORLD TRADE IN MERCHANDISE.

5—Adjusted figures. "Frontier values", dollar figures rounded off to the nearest ten million.

	$ (000,000's)				Percentage distribution		
	1928	1928 new $ gold	1935	1937	1928	1935	1937
Imports							
Foodsuffs and live animals	9,120	15,450	5,120	6,430	25·7	24·3	22·8
Materials, raw or partly manufactured	12,830	21,730	8,100	11,500	36·2	38·5	41·0
Manufactured articles ...	13,530	22,900	7,820	10,190	38·1	37·2	36·2
Total	35,480	60,080	21,040	28,170	100	100	100
Exports							
Foodstuffs and live animals	8,310	14,080	4,480	5,610	25·5	23·5	22·1
Materials, raw or partly manufactured.........	11,390	19,280	7,150	9,920	34·9	37·6	39·0
Manufactured articles ...	12,910	21,860	7,400	9,880	39·6	38·9	28·0
Total	32,610	55,220	19,030	25,410	100	100	100

From *Network of World Trade.*

On looking at these figures one remarks that the world imported more than it exported. The explanation is that imports are reckoned C.I.F. (i.e. cost plus insurance and freight charges) while exports are F.O.B. (free on board). This difference was about 9% in 1928 but rose to 12% by 1938 for various reasons.

The table is greatly elaborated in Table 7 which ought to be borne in mind for reference.

The table shows 'a marked shift in trade from foodstuffs to raw materials'. A few examples will suffice. In S.E. Asia the share of foodstuffs fell from 41% to 25% while raw materials rose from 54% to 71%. The export of raw materials for Brazil rose from 18% to 30%, while foodstuffs fell from 80% to 69% as cotton and sisal replaced coffee. This change over was due a good deal to two factors. The breakdown in world trade which began in 1929 was so severe that the industrial exporting countries could no longer find markets and were faced with a vast unemployment. They could not buy the raw materials and foodstuffs which the food producing and raw materials producing countries had for sale. The world was forced to witness the terrifying spectacle of starvation and misery in the midst of plenty: the Brazilians burning coffee, the Americans ploughing in cotton and killing off hogs, international conferences to limit the planting of cereals. Against this, in the industrialised countries, millions unemployed and factories idle. It is not our purpose here to analyse causes but to consider some of the results. Faced with such problems the governments of all countries had to do something. Much of what they did was far from wise, but again that is not the point here. Nearly all the policies put into motion aimed at greater self sufficiency. It is nearly always possible to increase food output even in the industrialised countries at a price and this was done though in some countries such as Germany and Italy the motive was strategical as well as economic. Whatever the reason the result was the same. A fall in imported foodstuffs. On the other hand it is harder and often impossible to increase and vary supplies of home produced raw materials. Take our own case, we have increased food supplies considerably since 1939 but are just as dependent as ever on imports for raw materials. The agricultural countries for their salvation turned more to industry with varying degrees of success.

The directions of world trade for 1935 and 1938 are set out in Table 17 in dollars and in percentages of the whole world in Table 18.

DIRECTION OF WORLD MERCHANDISE IMPORTS IN 1938 BY EIGHT GROUPS.

Percentages based on the absolute figures given in Table 17.

Imports of:

Imports from:	Africa	North America	Latin America	Asia	U.S.S.R.	Continental Europe	Non-Continental Europe	Oceania	Total
	%	%	%	%	%	%	%	%	%
Africa	0·4	0·3	—	0·2	—	3·0	1·2	—	5·1
North America	0·7	3·2	2·7	2·6	0·4	4·1	3·9	0·7	18·3
Latin America	0·1	2·5	1·4	0·1	—	3·4	1·9	—	9·4
Asia	0·7	2·7	0·3	6·2	0·2	3·1	2·2	0·5	15·9
U.S.S.R.	—	0·1	—	0·1	—	0·6	0·3	—	1·1
Continental Europe ..	2·8	2·3	2·5	2·4	0·3	19·7	5·3	0·3	35·6
Non-Continental Europe	1·6	1·0	0·9	1·8	0·2	3·3	0·8	1·4	11·0
Oceania	—	0·2	—	0·3	—	0·7	2·2	0·2	3·6
Total ...	6·3	12·3	7·8	13·7	1·1	37·9	17·8	3·1	100·0

From *Network of World Trade*, p. 40.

The reader will note that this is really an import-export table, but if it confuses, he had better neglect it. Certain facts, however, are useful to remember, and these are summarised in the 'Network' as follows:

"It will be seen that of world imports in that year, Continental Europe accounted for 38% (20% being trade amongst the countries of that group), and that 16% of world imports represented imports of other continents from Continental Europe. Thus, 54% of all trade in the year represented goods either imported from or by Continental Europe.

The corresponding figure for Non-Continental Europe was 28%, for total Europe 73%, for North America 27%, and for Europe and North America together 89%. Trade among the remaining continental groups thus amounted to only 11% of world trade. This preponderance of the trade of Europe and North America is further illustrated in Diagram 3."

We have taken three tables as examples of how to get to work. The first gave us trade in terms of dollars: the second divided that trade into three major categories, and the third has given us the relative importance of the continents in this total trade. We are now ready to take each area by itself. The procedure would be the same but instead of the world we have a 'group'. So one can work one's way along from the group to the individual country. One might in this exposition have started with the individual country and worked up to the world as a whole. After thought, one preferred the method of working down. Whichever way one proceeds, and there is much to be said for the other, one must always see the individual industrial and commercial activity in terms of the whole country, the country in the larger setting of the group and the group as part of the whole world. Only then can one begin to take a proper view. People get lost in details otherwise.

We will look briefly at Europe, tables and details for which are taken from *Europe's Trade*. As advised above read the Introduction which is a very condensed summary. Now look at the diagram, page 200.

Note the importance of Europe in 1938, before it had destroyed itself. It will explain a great deal of what is happening now. Europe with 4% of the land area: 19% of the world's population accounted had 56% of the world's imports and 46% of the exports, making 51% of the world's trade. The excess of imports over exports is chiefly accounted for by interest on investments and certain invisible items. This dominant position was slowly diminishing. At the beginning of the century 66% of all the trade was European: in 1913 it was still over 60%. After the first war the position declined partly because of the war and partly because the U.S. and other continents were developing.

This European trade was not equally spread.   Ten[1] industrial

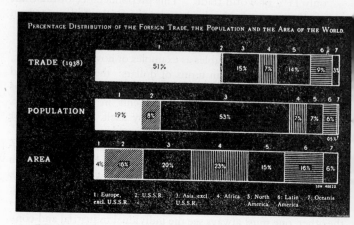

PERCENTAGE DISTRIBUTION OF THE FOREIGN TRADE, THE POPULATION AND THE AREA OF THE WORLD.

TRADE (1938) 51% 15% 7% 14% 9% 3%

POPULATION 19% 8% 53% 7% 7% 6%

AREA 4% 16% 20% 23% 15% 16% 6%

1: Europe, excl. U.S.S.R.   2: U.S.S.R.   3: Asia excl. U.S.S.R.   4: Africa   5: North America   6: Latin America   7: Oceania

countries stood out dominating that trade.   Look at the table opposite.

Not only do these ten countries dominate the situation but within the group two nations stand out, the United Kingdom and Germany.   There is half the key to the present problems.   The other half of the key or a considerable portion lies in the fact that the Eastern European countries are now on the Russian side of the new frontier so that co-operation is at the best very difficult. The present breakdown then turns largely upon (1) the fact that the U.K. has lost most of its overseas investments and so cannot buy in the quantities it did; also that the U.K. was a great supplier of fuel to the Continent and has ceased to be so; (2) that Germany as a great industrial nation has temporarily ceased to exist; (3) the acute political division of Europe retards economic advance.   That of course is not all.   The UNO Survey 1948 has an illuminating chapter on the problem of

[1] Austria, Belgium, Luxemburg, Czecho-Slovakia, France, Germany, Italy, Netherlands, Sweden, Switzerland and the U.K.

EUROPEAN COUNTRIES: TRADE WITH EUROPE AND
THE REST OF THE WORLD IN 1935.

	Imports			Exports		
	Share in the total imports of Europe[a]	Share of imports derived from		Share in the total exports of Europe[a]	Share of exports absorbed by	
		Europe[a]	Rest of World		Europe[a]	Rest of World
Highly industrialised countries:	%	%	%	%	%	%
United Kingdom	29·6	34	66	23·1	37	63
Germany	14·4	57	43	18·9	72	28
France	11·9	38	62	11·3	53	47
Belgium-Luxemburg	5·3	59	41	6·4	71	29
Netherlands	5·5	63	37	5·0	77	23
Italy	5·5	60	40	4·8	60	40
Sweden	3·2	79	21	3·6	75	25
Switzerland.....	3·5	79	21	2·8	79	21
Czecho-Slovakia	2·4	67	33	3·4	76	24
Austria	2·0	82	18	1·9	89	11
Total	83·3	49	51	81·2	60	40
Other countries:						
Denmark.......	2·4	85	15	2·9	96	4
Spain	2·4	54	46	2·1	70	30
Norway	1·7	72	28	1·6	72	28
Poland-Danzig .	1·4	64	36	1·9	85	15
Ireland.........	1·6	86	14	1·1	97	3
Hungary	1·0	90	10	1·5	92	8
Finland	1·0	74	26	1·5	80	20
Roumania	0·8	93	7	1·6	93	7
Yugoslavia ...	0·7	83	17	1·0	89	11
Greece	0·9	69	31	0·7	75	25
Portugal	0·9	70	30	0·5	71	29
Turkey	0·6	82	18	0·9	79	21
Bulgaria	0·3	97	3	0·4	93	7
Latvia	9·3	80	20	0·4	89	11
Lithuania	0·2	80	20	0·3	87	13
Estonia	0·2	73	27	0·3	92	8
Iceland	0·1	100	—	0·1	88	12
Albania	0·0	82	18	0·0	86	14
Various minor areas	0·2	.	.	0·0	.	.
Total	16·7	75	25	18·8	85	15
Total Europe (excluding U.S.S.R.)	100	54	46	100	64	36
U.S.S.R.	[b]1·8	57	43	[b]3·5	74	26

[a] Excluding U.S.S.R.
[b] Imports (exports) of the U.S.S.R. as percentage of the Imports of Europe
excluding U.S.S.R.   *Europe's Trade*, p. 16.

Inter-European Trade which again is much too full for the
beginner. Some members of Parliament might read it with
profit on both sides of the House; so might many others in still
more dominant positions for influencing this nation's and
Europe's welfare. We will content ourselves with the two
opening paragraphs which give the key to the chapter.

"Among the conclusions that have emerged from the analysis
up to this point are the following: that intra-European trade
is lagging seriously behind European recovery in general;
that a large part of the contraction is in the goods previously
sold to or supplied by Germany; that trade among other
European countries is also lagging; that the decline in trade
within Europe is one of the chief reasons for Europe's
extraordinary post-war requirements from overseas; and
that one of the pre-conditions of the cure of Europe's acute
external disequilibrium is the restoration of intra-European
trade.

"It is obvious from the outset that the restoration of intra-
European trade cannot be dissociated from the restoration of
European production—i.e. that production itself is the chief
limitation on trade. The problem of increasing production
will be examined in the next chapter. But evidence is
accumulating in the work of the Economic Commission for
Europe, and elsewhere, that there are other important
limiting factors on intra-European trade arising from the
conditions under which that trade is conducted, and that
economic recovery in Europe must be approached from the
standpoint of improving the trading framework as well as
from the standpoint of increasing production in the various
separate national economies."

Special emphasis should be laid on the statement that intra-
European trade cannot be dissociated from production. It
brings one back to what we insisted upon at the beginning of
this chapter: that international trade is only a part of that much
greater whole, industry. You cannot trade if you have nothing

to trade with. One always comes back to production. All planning must be tested by this measure: does it increase production? Rationing is not planning except negatively. It is stopping people doing things, eating things, using things, travelling. The test is production.

We must now turn to the single country but will deal with it in the next chapter.

CHAPTER XII

THE TRADE OF GREAT BRITAIN

THIS chapter must perforce be statistical as at some point we must come down to figures. It will not only serve its immediate purpose of discussing the foreign trade of Great Britain, but might go to show how very slightly and perfunctorily we have dealt with the larger units of continental and world trade.

For references I suggest the *Annual Abstract of Statistics* which has been mentioned already.[1] References will be made to it but beginners can ignore them though others would be well advised to take the trouble to look them up. All the tables are exceedingly clear and helpful. I have given particular references for No. 84, but readers will easily find their way in any later numbers as the format and numbering will not vary greatly. Foreign Trade tables come in Section VIII under the title Trade—External. These tables go back to 1935 and give a perspective which is very necessary as no one year can be taken in isolation. There is a danger of unconsciously taking 1935 or 1938 as a 'normal' base. One should be on one's guard against this as neither year has any claim to such distinction. The tables given below are taken from the *Board of Trade Journal* which is published weekly and which can generally be found in library reading rooms. If not ask for one. Early each year there is published an analysis of our foreign trade, generally in two consecutive numbers in January.[2] The reader would be wise to obtain copies for study and use. Finally the White Paper, Cmd 7324, United Kingdom Balance of Payments 1946 and 1947.[3] The data are as full as the reader will wish, some may think too full but it is hard to discuss the vast trade of this country with less. All one can do in the present limited space is to call attention to a few of the more important points.

---

[1] No. 84, 1935–46 published 1948 at 10/-.
[2] The references here are to Nos. 2,666–7: price 6d. each.
[3] Price 2d.

First in the Abstract read the printed note which briefly tells you that the imports are valued C.I.F., while exports are F.O.B. Then note that the Retained Imports, i.e. Imports less Re-exports amounted to £1,247 million in 1946. Compare this for the figure in the White Paper and you find they don't agree, that figure being £1,092 million, but you have been warned. The White Paper figure is F.O.B. Why the difference? That's just bureaucratic fun. These additional charges —insurance and freight—vary from time to time but the average percentage addition is usually from 10 to 11%. The London and Cambridge Economic Service give 14% for 1946 and this would make the two totals correspond. Even if they didn't they are near enough for our present purpose. Turn now to Table 215 in the Abstract Value and Volume of the external trade of the U.K. of which a modified version is given here.

	1935	1938	1939	1942	1946	1947
Value (£ million)						
(Retained) Imports	701	858	840	992	1,247	1,728
Exports	426	471	440	271	912	1,137
Volume Index (1938–100)						
Imports		92·6	100·0	97·0	70·0	67·0	77·4
Exports		103·2	100·0	94·0	36·0	99·0	108·5

The heading of the article in the *Board of Trade Journal* is 'Value of Exports in 1947, Highest except for 1920'. Many people only seem to read headlines so that such a heading is dangerous. If, however, one reads on one comes to the paragraph, "The value of exports of U.K. goods in 1947 was, apart from 1920, the highest on record and nearly 2½ times the 1938 figure. In terms of volume, however, exports were less than one tenth higher than in that year, the provisional volume index for 1947 being 108". There is no need to be misled if one takes the trouble to read, though no mention is made of the increase in the population by some 2¼ million. The first task then is to find out what is the value of money. The gratifying increase in our trade is largely due to the fall in the purchasing power of the pound.   Actually we know the pound is less valuable, but we tend to forget it when looking over a period of years. Then the index volume.   This is a complicated affair which we must leave at that.   It does however give a rough idea of what is happening.

The Abstract then gives more elaborate tables first in value and then in quantities, Tables 217 to 223 inclusive.   These are particularly useful and very clear.   Even those who are afraid of figures are urged to look at them.   First, Table 218, value of retained imports.   The division is into three major categories— the Brussels classification.   (1) Food, drink, and tobacco, (2) Raw materials and articles mainly unmanufactured, (3) Articles wholly or mainly manufactured.   There are two other headings which can normally be neglected.   (4) Animals not for food and (5) Parcel Post.   In pre-war days these were so slight they could be neglected though of late Parcel Post has grown and was £15,000,000 in 1947.   These major headings are then sub-divided so that one can get some idea what kind of commodity is being imported.   Table 219 deals with the exports in the same way.   I shall neglect re-exports for lack of space.   There are then tables analysing imports and exports by countries of source and destination.   These make the division first into British and Foreign and one sees the relative importance of Empire and non-Empire trading.   Roughly half our trade is outside the Empire, a very important thing to remember when planning trade.   The second division (in the same tables) divides the trade between continents so that one can get a quick view of which way it is going and of the relative importance of the sources and destinations.   One notices the dominant part played by the Americas, particularly the U.S. and Canada, in our import trade, and how little they matter for our exports.   The third division gives the countries themselves.   One can thus get an expanding view of the picture.

Tables 222 and 223 give the same type of analysis as 218 and 219 but this time in commodities.   These make very interesting reading and help one to understand the necessity for rationing.   It is both illuminating and confusing as one is faced with a great mass of detail.   The only thing to do at first is to pick out a few commodities as types: gradually as one gets more advanced and experienced one can extend the range and depth of inquiries. Let us see where we now stand. There is the table giving the money value of our foreign trade. That seems to paint a bright picture until we discover that the pounds are not worth so much as in 1938. Then we have the tables dividing the trade into three major categories and then by countries of origin and destination. Lastly we check up by looking at the tables of actual quantities. Now we can begin. Let us look at the table below taken from the *Board of Trade Journal*.[1]

PERCENTAGE OF TRADE: MAJOR CATEGORIES

Board of Trade Journal, 31.1.48, p. 218.

Class	Per cent of total		
	1938	1946	1947
Food, drink and tobacco	46·8	49·0	45·1
Raw materials and articles mainly unmanufactured	27·0	30·0	31·3
Articles wholly or mainly manufactured	25·4	18·9	22·3

Certain facts stand out: more than three-quarters of our import trade is in foodstuffs and in raw materials, none of which we can do without. In spite of what we have done to encourage agriculture, 45 % of our imports were food, drink and tobacco. Can we trace any connection between this persistent percentage —it was 46·8 in 1938—and the attempt to be less dependent upon outside supplies? Before the war we imported 5,465,000 tons of wheat and flour, and produced at home 1,965,000, making in all 7,430,000 tons. In 1943 home supplies had in-

[1] *Journal* 31.1.48, p. 218.

creased to 3,447,000 tons which was our maximum output of
wheat. Imports fell accordingly. By 1946 the home grown
wheat had dropped to 1,967,000 tons and imports were 3,907,000
tons making a total of 5,874,000 tons[1]. Notice that the consumption figure is fairly steady though there were 2,250,000
more mouths to be fed compared with 1938. Slightly less per
head but not necessarily per human mouth as we were wasteful
in 1938. May I commend readers to turn to Tables 201, 202, and
203 in the Abstract which give the acreages of the principal
crops and the total outputs. Table 203 gives the estimated
yield per acre which is most important. It shows that in spite of
talk average yields have not gone up just as the total quantities
produced shown in the previous table are quite inadequate to
maintain anything like a sufficient and decent diet for 50,000,000
people.

Now consider the table opposite.[2]

In 1938 there were imported 1,548,000 tons of meat and in
1947, 1,403,000. In the same years home production was
1,303,000 and 986,000[3] respectively. Of butter we imported
in 1938, 476,000 tons and in 1947, 216,000, while in those years
home produced butter was 20,000 and 11,000 tons respectively.

Enough has been said to show that given our present techniques of agricultural production, imports of food must take a
high and urgent place in our foreign trade and life. Unless
there are very great changes in the techniques of farming, in
mechanising and in supplying far more fertilisers, outputs per
acre will not go up nor will high wages and decent living
conditions for the farm workers be possible.

Beverages prove to be chiefly tea, cocoa and coffee; wine
in 1946 was only two-thirds the import figure for 1938, though
spirits had almost quadrupled. Except for these which might
be excluded, the rest are regarded as necessaries and even demo-
crats are known to drink wine and spirits. Dare we suggest
the elimination of tobacco or even a reduction in the amount
consumed to the 1938 figure?

[1] The Government rather slipped up on wheat in 1946, hence the B.U.'s.
[2] B. of T. Journal, 1947, p. 218.
[3] 1946.

Commodity	Quantity				Value
	1938	1945	1946	1947	1947
	Thousand tons				£ million
Wheat	5,081	3,552	3,372	4,195	91·4
Flour	384	543	535	894	27·3
Rice, other grains and pulses	1,454	338	292	341	11·1
Maize and maize meal	3,028	510	119	482	10·4
Oilseed cake and meal	663	190	57	316	11·0
Other animal feeding stuffs..	1,241	10	59	196	3·5
Cattle for food*	259	179	161	157	11·9
Meat:—					
Beaf and veal	631	222	427	542	44·1
Mutton and lamb	357	378	425	441	37·4
Bacon and hams	377	244	179	132	21·0
Canned meat	73	97	188	187	27·2
Other descriptions	110	226	138	101	17·6
Butter	476	190	211	216	42·9
Cheese	146	191	204	192	31·5
Eggs in shell	191	48	56	80	13·5
Eggs not in shell:—					
Dried whole	0	36	46	34	23·8
Other	48	1	15	13	2·3
Condensed milk	82	65	91	71	5·7
Milk powder	18	30	37	51	4·4
Apples	353	30	92	76	3·4
Bananas	305	1	102	104	5·0
Oranges	538	306	266	412	17·8
Pears..................	67	0	46	105	7·2
Tomatoes...............	143	7	96	190	17·5
Raisins	83	81	81	74	5·9
Tinned or bottled fruit	218	38	49	90	6·4
Other fruit and vegetables ..	920	219	385	819	50·6
Sugar	2,406	1,066	1,469	1,877	59·1
Tea†	206	171	157	167	43·2
Cocoa, raw	132	95	125	107	13·2
Coffee	20	48	33	44	5·7
	Thousand proof gallons				
Spirits..................	2,676	6,721	7,477	9,283	6·9
	Thousand gallons				
Wine	15,901	3,800	8,477	11,115	10·3
	Thousand tons				
Other beverages	182	145	144	158	7·8
Fish:—					
Fresh or frozen..........	82	229	203	214	12·4
Other (including canned)	104	47	88	88	16·0
Other foods..............	919	456	413	692	30·0
Tobacco................	155	165	194	132	47·4
Total of food, drink and Tobacco................	21,562	10,198	10,636	14,076	805·4

    * Estimated weight.   † Retained imports.

The whole of the table should be examined, but good as it is it cannot tell the whole story. It must be taken with the figures already mentioned for home production. Foreign trade must always be studied as a part of the greater whole.

This great division accounts for just under one-third of our imports. The same inevitable need is revealed. Only coal can we supply for ourselves. Iron ore, but never in adequate amounts. After that all the metals must be imported. Of fibres wool is the only one which we supply in any amount and even this is wholly inadequate. In 1938 home produced wool was roughly 50,000 tons against 279,000 imported, and of the home product $\frac{1}{3}$ to $\frac{1}{2}$ was exported while the wool of the mountain sheep went to carpet making. Only about 10% of the wool used in the woollen and worsted industry came from the home supply. Since then home supplies have diminished. No country is more dependent upon raw materials than we. These cannot be stinted as without materials the best equipped factories and the most skilled labour are useless. Here notice the difference between ourselves and say the U.S. or Canada. These two countries largely supply their own foodstuffs and a large amount of their raw materials. Japan on the contrary is like ourselves, almost wholly dependent upon imported raw materials and that is why the Americans want the Japanese back in trade.

RAW AND SEMI-MANUFACTURED MATERIALS[1]

Commodity	Quantity				Value
	1938	1945	1946	1947	1947
	Thousand tons				£ million
Raw materials:—					
Coal	9	1	7	694	3·4
Asbestos	51	67	54	67	2·5
Iron ore	5,164	4,071	6,601	6,884	18·9
Tin ore and concentrates	55	45	47	39	9·3
Hardwood	953	400	370	783	14·4
Softwood	4,891	2,033	2,045	3,615	68·6
Pitprops	2,054	484	1,377	1,939	15·2
Wood pulp	1,618	677	815	768	23·0
Cotton†	518	386	344	304	49·2
Sheep's and lambs' wool†	279	191	172	210	41·8
Flax	41	18	19	28	6·6
Hemp and hemp tow	87	89	84	90	7·0
Jute†	160	87	74	64	5·3
Palm kernels	133	293	356	364	12·0
Other oilseeds and nuts	1,496	762	695	592	21·2
Linseed oil	19	8	60	112	19·2
Other vegetable oils	195	146	158	265	21·5
Whale oil	226	46	67	146	12·2
Other animal and fish oils	46	40	34	45	6·2
Rubber (crude and synthetic)†	132	63	250	112	13·9
Cattle hides†	51	89	87	124	21·1
Sheep and lamb skins	27	17	28	27	6·0
	Thousand cwts.				
Undressed fur skins (other than rabbit)	77	19	39	26	7·3
Semi-manufactured materials:—	Thousand tons				
Semi-finished steel*	353	81	309	213	4·4
Finished steel	479	34	47	92	4·1
Aluminium	46	21	83	96	6·7
Unwrought copper†	260	144	285	362	41·1
Unwrought lead	407	176	157	194	13·9
Unwrought zinc	165	97	55	149	8·9
Plywood	272	210	192	271	12·4
Paper and board	1,071	339	326	497	21·7

* Blooms, billets, slabs and sheet bars.
† Retained imports.
[1] B. of T. *Journal*, No. 2267, p. 220.

H

Articles Wholly or Mainly Manufactured[1]

		1938	1946	1947
III.—Articles Wholly or Mainly Manufactured—				
A.	Coke and manufactured fuel ...	8	12	122
B.	Pottery, glass, abrasives, etc....	7,187	1,895	6,353
C.	Iron and steel and manufactures thereof	14,816	9,352	14,966
D.	Non-ferrous metals and manufactures thereof	40,817	40,780	79,256
E.	Cutlery, hardware, implements and instruments.............	7,062	3,009	5,125
F.	Electrical goods and apparatus .	3,156	5,037	2,298
G.	Machinery	21,839	13,519	29,606
H.	Manufactures of wood and timber	6,287	9,857	16,879
I.	Cotton yarns and manufactures.	3,135	1,653	17,394
J.	Woollen and worsted yarns and manufactures	3,838	4,333	7,976
K.	Silk and artificial silk yarns and manufactures	4,946	2,252	8,556
L.	Manufactures of other textile materials	4,606	10,431	15,924
M.	Apparel	8,028	1,643	3,380
N.	Footwear	2,794	799	2,718
O.	Chemicals, drugs, dyes and colours	13,613	17,789	26,740
P.	Oils, fats and resins, manufactured	44,071	82,504	92,413
Q.	Leather and manufactures thereof	6,440	10,072	15,734
R.	Paper, cardboard, etc...........	14,842	11,882	21,745
S.	Vehicles (including locomotives, ships and aircraft)	4,533	2,699	6,037
T.	Rubber manufactures	681	29	154
U.	Miscellaneous articles wholly or mainly manufactured	20,823	15,724	26,048
	Total, Class III	233,522	245,271	399,424
IV.—Animals, not for Food		3,318	7,145	7,726
V.—Parcel Post		4,339	20,918	15,071
	Total, all Classes	919,509	1,301,030	7,187,471

[1] B. of T. *Journal*, No. 2666, p. 163.

This group was 22·3% of the total in 1947 as compared with 25·4% in 1938. The change is not very great in spite of Government control. At first sight this group might offer more scope for reduction than the first two. Can we not manufacture for ourselves? This is quite a different matter to supplying raw materials or even foodstuffs. The *Journal* deals with this group in an apparently perfunctory way. It has half a column devoted to it and no special tables. At first sight it would almost appear that the writer got tired and that the article had just petered out. The opening sentence, too, is puzzling, "The value of the imports of finished consumer goods other than food, drink and tobacco, amounted to £25·8 million compared with £11·7 million in 1946 and £32·7 million in 1938". That brings one up against the generally pre-conceived idea that the goods in the third group being manufactured are therefore 'consumer' goods. Look at the list and it becomes apparent that it contains a great mass of goods which are as important to our industry as the raw materials, etc. The largest single item is Oils, fats and resins, £92,413,000. What is the difference between processing, being semi-manufactured and manufactured? According as you define these terms so do the goods move in and out of their present classifications. Could we reduce this figure? Will the building of the new vast oil refineries make a great difference? The next longest is Chemicals, drugs, dyes and colours, £26,740,000. What are I.C.I. doing? Could they supply all these things? Evidently not at the moment and not at a proper price, otherwise they would not be imported. One does not import goods which one can produce at home as good in quality or as cheaply. So one goes down the list. All this, however, leads to something very important to us armchair economists. It is not sufficient to read books, we must go and find out. One does not know which is the more dangerous to himself or society, the man who only reads books or the man who never does. Anyhow books are not life. A perfect example of the bookworm is to be found in Burton's *Anatomy of Melancholy*, well worth reading for entertainment, but a hopeless jumble of untested statements. Find out what these imports really are by referring to the longer reports but more particularly by asking business men and industrialists

what is included under these numerous headings. If we accept
the *Journal* statement, and we can, the possible savings in consumer goods as contrasted with producer goods is slight,
£26,000,000. Even then analysis reveals that £3·3 million went
in books, etc. Not really enough. Footwear was not much and
there are some feet British manufacturers refuse to cater for.
It would be a grave and dangerous thing to exclude all consumer
goods as from such competition comes a good deal of the urge
to the home manufacturer. Iron curtains are just as disastrous
in these matters as in ideas. These then are the imports:

			£
I.	Food, etc.		805,427,000
II.	Raw Materials, etc.		559,823,000
III.	Manufactures		399,424,000
IV & V.	Animals & Parcel Post		22,797,000
			1,787,471,000
Re-exports would reduce the total to			1,688,304,000

We turn now to exports which should be approached in the
same manner and order. The Statistical Abstract has tables of
the same kind as already mentioned for the imports. We will
proceed in the same order but more briefly:[1]

Description	Per cent. of total			
	1938	1946	First half 1947	Second half 1947
Food, drink and tobacco	7·6	7·0	5·4	5·9
Raw materials and articles mainly unmanufactured	12·1	3·6	3·7	2·4
Articles wholly or mainly manufactured Of which:—	77·6	86·3	87·5	88·1
Metals	37·3	44·2	47·0	49·5
Textiles.....................	21·5	20·4	20·5	19·2
Other manufactures	18·8	21·8	20·0	19·4

[1] B. of T. *Journal*, No. 2666, p. 162.

One notices how small a part is played by exports under headings I and II, and how completely Class III dominates the table. This predominance of manufactures in our exports is even greater than at first sight appears for a considerable part of the values in I could just as well come under III. It includes biscuits, refined sugar, sweets, beer, cocoa and chocolate as well as manufactured tobacco. Class II is much more what it appears to be—raw materials. Before the war this class was more important than today, but because of one commodity, coal. In 1939 these exports were valued at £54,400,000 of which coal accounted for £38,300,000 and the pound bought more then. Here is a chance for the Coal Board and the miners.

Class III Manufactures given below is very compressed but can be filled out by those who so desire. The *Journal* gives a number of excellent tables.

Note the dominating positions of iron and steel, machinery and vehicles which account for half of our exports. These break up into a multitude of commodities, details of which are given in the *Board of Trade Journal*.[1] They can be found also for past years in the Abstract, Table 223, pp. 189–192. Note also how the textiles have declined in quantity since 1937 and that was a poor showing compared with 1912, but the glory has departed. Compare cotton exports at 531 million square yards with 6,913 linear yards in 1912 (1 linear yards was slightly more than a square yard). It measures the degree of ruin of the Lancashire cotton industry. Wool has declined much less and is slowly recovering. Rayon alone shows some vitality. Last of all look at the miscellaneous group which makes quite a useful figure, nearly £69,000,000. This is made up of hundreds of small things. One mentions it because the miscellaneous items in trade returns altogether are important. Too often we tend to forget this. Many of these miscellaneous exports are in just those little things where old skill and crafstmanship count. A country like ours ought to have a paternal eye for such things for they not only help the trade balance but keep these skills alive: craftsmen are always worth while. Crafts educate and

[1] At end of chapter.

[1] III. ARTICLES WHOLLY OR MAINLY MANUFACTURED:—	1938	1946	1947
A. Coke and manufactured fuel	3,292	1,076	182
B. Pottery, glass, abrasives, etc.	9,610	27,621	32,841
C. Iron and steel and manufactures thereof	41,692	80,021	84,298
D. Non-ferrous metals and manufactures thereof	12,339	37,625	40,384
E. Cutlery, hardware, implements and instruments	9,028	26,901	35,299
F. Electrical goods and apparatus ...	13,611	37,735	49,425
G. Machinery	57,868	114,749	180,544
H. Manufactures of wood and timber	1,165	1,541	1,539
I. Cotton yarns and manufactures ..	49,681	63,180	77,655
J. Woollen and worsted yarns and manufactures	26,814	43,613	57,925
K. Silk and artificial silk yarns and manufactures	5,502	27,371	29,526
L. Manufactures of other textile materials	10,657	21,806	28,000
M. Apparel.....................	8,515	30,463	31,726
N. Footwear	1,963	5,020	6,726
O. Chemicals, drugs, dyes and colours	22,280	66,085	67,413
P. Oils, fats and resins, manufactured	5,365	6,424	8,153
Q. Leather and manufactures thereof	3,943	6,066	7,022
R. Paper, cardboard, etc............	6,930	14,409	17,197
S. Vehicles (including locomotives, ships and aircraft)	44,491	114,998	168,098
T. Rubber manufactures	1,650	5,559	6,310
U. Miscellaneous articles wholly or mainly manufactured	28,849	56,847	68,614
TOTAL, CLASS III	365,245	789,110	998,877
IV.—ANIMALS, NOT FOR FOOD	679	3,758	3,574
V.—PARCEL POST	12,017	25,134	35,700
TOTAL, ALL CLASSES	470,755	914,699	1,137,083

[1] B. of T. Journal, p. 165.

make men wise and happy: mass production robs labour of its dignity and educative power and so makes for discontented and frustrated lives.

The direction of our foreign trade is as important as the volume, for it affects the supply of dollars among other things. This shortage of dollars is only another and easy way of saying, (1) that we are overtrading, and (2) that the direction of our trading has been diverted and twisted so that the pattern has been spoilt. The first reason is very much within our own control: the second is not. The tables below show the direction of our export and of our imports in percentages.

EXPORTS [1]

Area	Percentage of total value			
	1938	1946	1947	Fourth Quarter 1947
France and Northern Europe	29·75	30·53	26·27	26·95
Rest of Europe	6·84	7·61	7·80	7·57
Africa	15·64	17·61	16·77	16·34
India and Western Asia	10·23	14·74	14·42	13·33
Rest of Asia	6·36	5·25	7·63	6·99
Oceania	12·35	9·16	10·21	11·61
North America	9·34	7·54	8·16	8·53
Central America and West Indies ..	2·23	1·97	1·92	2·01
South America...................	7·26	5·59	6·82	6·67
Total, British Countries	49·86	49·24	52·73	54·38
Total, Foreign Countries	50·14	50·76	47·27	45·62
Total, All Countries	100·00	100·00	100·00	100·00

[1] B. of T. Journal, 21 Feb. 48, p. 390.

IMPORTS [1]

Area	Percentage of total value			
	Year 1938	Year 1946	Year 1947	Fourth Quarter 1947
France and Northern Europe	28·52	13·91	16·11	18·35
Rest of Europe	5·00	3·96	4·54	3·49
Africa	6·89	9·81	9·65	9·92
India and Western Asia	8·63	10·04	8·67	10·53
Rest of Asia	4·80	2·42	2·95	2·89
Oceania	13·13	10·96	10·61	10·34
North America	21·68	33·12	29·71	27·75
Central America and West Indies ..	3·78	5·85	6·28	5·49
South America..................	7·57	9·93	11·48	11·24
Total, British Countries	40·41	48·71	45·11	46·30
Total, Foreign Countries	59·59	51·29	54·89	53·70
Total, All Countries	100·00	1000·0	100·00	100·00

B. of T. *Journal*, 21 Feb. 48, p. 391.

Now look at the trade in sterling.

PRINCIPAL EXPORT MARKETS [1]

Country	1938	1946	1947	Order of Importance	
				1938	1946
	£ million	£ million	£ million		
Union of South Africa	39·5	75·3	91·8	1	2
India, Pakistan, etc.*	33·8	79·7	91·6	3	1
Australia	38·2	55·2	71·8	2	3
Eire	20·3	39·6	55·9	7	5
United States of America ...	20·5	35·5	47·9	6	6
Canada	22·5	32·6	43·4	4	8
New Zealand	19·2	27·9	43·1	9	10
Argentine Republic	19·3	20·5	34·7	8	15
Belgium	8·2	27·0	33·6	17	11
Netherlands	13·1	30·9	30·8	12	9
British Malaya.............	11·1	20·3	30·1	14	16
Sweden	11·7	21·4	29·9	13	13

* Formerly British India.
[1] B. of T. *Journal*, 21 Feb. 48, p. 391.

PRINCIPAL SOURCES OF IMPORTS [1]

Country	1938	1946	1947	Order of Importance	
				1938	1946
	£ million	£ million	£ million		
United States of America ...	118·0	229·6	294·9	1	1
Canada	78·7	195·9	230·3	2	2
Argentine Republic	38·5	66·7	130·7	6	6
Australia	71·8	67·4	97·1	3	5
India, Pakistan, etc.*	49·9	69·0	94·4	4	4
New Zealand	46·9	74·4	89·6	5	3
British West Africa	9·3	36·1	53·0	24	8
Sweden	25·5	32·4	41·1	10	9
Cuba	4·8	20·5	40·3	35	16
Belgium	18·6	14·7	35·5	15	22
Eire	23·0	37·1	35·2	12	7
Dutch West Indies	14·7	25·6	34·8	16	12

* Formerly British India.
[1] B. of T. Journal, 21 Feb. 48, p. 392.

One has been brief as space is lacking and there is still much to comment on. If you turn to the White Paper: U.K. Balance of Payments 1946 and 1947[1] you will be presented with the total accounts of the country as a trader. So far we have been dealing with visible trade, i.e. the trade which goes through the customs. This, very obviously, is not all the story. Economists distinguish between two terms 'the balance of trade' with which we have been dealing, and 'the balance of accounts' which includes the balance of trade and many other items often termed 'invisible' trade. That is trade which is not tangible. It is the balance of accounts which matters. Too often, especially in the past, people have employed the term 'favourable or unfavourable' balance of trade as if a favourable balance, i.e. an excess of exports over imports, is a good thing while an unfavourable balance, i.e. an excess of imports over exports, is a bad one. If they were applied to the 'balance of accounts' the terms would make sense. There is no harm in so using the words provided one remembers

[1] Cmd. 7324.

H*

UNITED KINGDOM BALANCE OF PAYMENTS
1946 and 1947

TABLE I

CURRENT ACCOUNT

£ millions

	1938	1946	1947 Provisional
Payments			
1. Imports (f.o.b.)	835	1,092	1,574
2. Government expenditure—			
(*a*) Military (net)	...	230	80
(*b*) Relief and rehabilitation	...	110	62
(*c*) Cost of Germany (net) .	...	40	79
(*d*) Other (net)	...	−90	−10
Total Government expenditure	16	290	211
3. Shipping	80	140	163
4. Interest, profits and dividends.	30	77	94
5. Film remittances (net)	7	17	13
6. Tourist payments	40	26	50
7. Total payments	1,008	1,642	2,105
Receipts			
8. Exports and re-exports (f.o.b.)	533	888	1,125
9. Shipping	100	149	180
10. Interest, profits and dividends .	205	152	145
11. Other (net).................	100	73	−20
11. Total receipts	938	1,262	1,430
Surplus (+) or Deficit (−) on Current Account			
13. With Sterling Area	...	−30	+80
14. With Western Hemisphere ..	...	−360	−680
15. With Rest of World	...	+10	−75
16. Total	−70	−380	−675

that they refer only to visible trade. Thus Great Britain has had an 'unfavourable' balance of trade for quite a century, while the U.S. has had a 'favourable' balance. Actually a little thought will convince one that a nation in the long run, like an individual, must pay for what it buys. It can overtrade for a time: can borrow for a time but sooner or later, and generally sooner, it must face facts or the facts will face it. Somehow it must balance its accounts.

Look at the figures for 1938. Items 3–6 make up the invisible trade. In that year we paid £157,000,000 for shipping services, tourists payments, films, interest and profits but in the opposite direction for similar things received £405,000,000. There was a net balance on the 'invisible' side of £248,000,000, which helped to offset the deficit in the visible trading. It was not enough, however, and there was a net deficit in the total trading of £70,000,000 which came out of capital account.

These 'invisible' items are estimates, not accurate figures. They are subject to revision so that when comparing with past years one must be on the alert. The Board of Trade publish a provisional estimate each year and this is corrected later. Today with greater statistical knowledge the figures are pretty accurate and can be accepted for purposes such as ours.

When will a country have a 'favourable' and when an 'unfavourable' balance of trade? That will depend upon a number of factors, a few of which are mentioned here.

1. An old creditor country will generally have an unfavourable balance as it will be receiving interest on its investments.

2. A 'young' country may borrow capital goods for a few years with which to develop its resources. The import of these capital goods may cause trade to be unfavourable for a time, but debtor countries in general must have favourable balances as they have to pay interest on their borrowings as well as pay for their imports.

3. A creditor country if it is still lending heavily and in excess of the incoming interest may have a favourable balance but one day the balance is bound to turn. No country can lend money for ever and have a favourable balance.

4. In addition to the borrowing and lending of capital there

exists a series of other payments such as those already mentioned in the White Paper though these are not all. Others are, (1) remittances sent by immigrants to the old country, a large item against the U.S. and a pleasant one for such countries as Italy and Ireland, though now sadly diminishing. Thus in 1929 U.S. paid out under this one heading[1] $288,000,000. (2) Institutional payments such as those made to missions, charities, etc. The vast sums recently lent and being lent by the U.S. to ourselves and Europe imply a 'favourable' balance. For those who wish there is a Table in *The U.S. in the World Economy*[1] giving a complete analysis of U.S. world transactions. Italy used partly to balance her accounts by tourist receipts and emigrant remittances.

This invisible trade has played a large and important role in the economic life of our country. Thus in 1928 the net interest received was £289,000,000, while shipping and other items came to £210,000,000. It is the loss of these which is the immediate cause of our present troubles. In 1946, the total debit balance was estimated to be £380,000,000 and in 1947 at £675,000,000. If one makes allowances for the fall in the value of money this adverse balance is largely explained in the loss of these investments and in the fall in shipping receipts due to war losses.

To understand our present position properly, however, it is necessary to go a little further back. Victorian England, unlike ourselves, not only lived on its earnings but had a surplus for investment and this surplus was invested yearly abroad. It may be argued, with considerable force, that they would have done better to invest it at home in human lives, but the point is, they didn't. The economic soul of the Victorians is well depicted in Smiles' books *Self-help*, *Thrift*, *Character*, *Duty*, four repulsive titles which contrast strongly with the popular and colourful ones of today. Maybe they were too austere though they reflect the age and the upbringing of the man, for Smiles was the "eldest of eleven children left, on their father's death, to be supported by their mother on slender means." They got through, he becoming a doctor. May a late Victorian recommend these books, they are still worth reading. But whether

[1] *The U.S. in the World Economy*, Stationery Office, 1944.

the Victorians were penny wise and pound foolish is not our theme. What does matter is that they saved and invested until by 1913 the net income from investments was £210,000,000 all in really worth-while pounds. They had a net balance of about £181,000,000 so they were more than self supporting. By that time Victorian austerity was passing into Edwardian urbanity. As already mentioned the nation invested less and less abroad after the World War, living like a 'gentleman' partly on its earned income and partly on its investments until at last it was living on capital. Such a life is reflected in the patterns of industry and of consumption. The psychological effect however was bad. Englishmen imagined their standards of living were based upon their superior industrial and commercial worth whereas they were not, being partly based upon their ancestors' work and thrift. Today that foolish attitude has become almost pathological when the standards are maintained by overseas' charity and the recipient is not even grateful, but what paupers are? There is an excellent analytical table of the balance of payments in the *National Provincial Bank Review* for August 1948. The net shipping income for 1938 as given in the table does not agree with that in the White Paper. There is a difference of £80,000,000 which can be explained by the fact that the White Paper figures are F.O.B. and those given by the bank are C.I.F.

A consumption pattern must eventually be made to fit the production pattern or rather it is a mutual adaption. Our problem even with the best will is immensely difficult for in the near future we must once more 'keep' ourselves. This we have seen can only be done if we can import raw materials of all kinds in vast quantities and also the greater part of our foodstuffs. To pay for these we must export on an ever-increasing scale. Today in spite of our efforts we are still far from being self supporting and that on a seller's market. The real test will come in the next few years. A nation such as ours can only hope to retain its markets then by a combination of the utmost skill and the finest managerial ability combined with a high morale on the part of both work-people and managers. It will demand a high educational standard and some Victorian austerity.

The problem is not insoluble, but the solution lies more in the realms of morals than economics. The economic difficulties are great and obvious, but are definitely amenable and could be overcome within a decade if we had faith combined with work.

A final remark on what is called the 'terms of trade', that is the rates at which we exchange exports for imports. The Board of Trade issue these from time to time and they are here produced[1]

Barclay's Bank Review. August 1948, p. 49.
Index Numbers, 1938 = 100

	Average values of U.K. imports	Average values of U.K. exports	Terms of Trade
1913	97	68	142
1924	150	129	116
1929	130	109	119
1933	83	87	95
1934	86	88	98
1935	89	89	100
1938	100	100	100
1946	211	196	108
1947	258	222	116

Note:—The figures under the heading 'Terms of Trade' above, show the changes in the volume of exports required to pay for a fixed volume of imports, i.e. a rise in the index indicates an adverse movement in the terms of trade. These figures can only give an approximate measure of the fluctuations in the terms of trade, owing mainly to variations in the make-up of imports and exports and to uneven fluctuations in the prices of particular commodities.

Note that 1938 is taken as the base. The terms of trade have moved steadily against us though it is interesting to see that they have generally been so according to the table and we are no worse off than in 1930. Actually 1938 has no particular merits and is merely taken as the last full pre-war year. The terms are likely to move against us still further. The Govern-

[1] *Barclay's Bank Review*, Aug. 48, p. 49.

ment (this is not politics, any Government would have done the same) is gambling on the terms moving in our favour and the nation is gladly backing them. It seems unlikely they will. Even if import prices do fall it is highly likely that export prices will also fall. The reader is warned that these average values of imports and exports are very tricky calculations so that the final ratio is of a similar nature to the parent which begat it.

BIBLIOGRAPHY

As the reader will have seen, I have mentioned in the text the various books to which I wish him to refer and to which I have referred but it might be useful to tabulate them for reference. A few I have not included as the reference was only incidental, a few others I have added but it is not my intention to do more than this. The choice is often a very arbitrary one such as any teacher or tutor must make.

The general reader need not bother too much about the references though I suggest a few books which are fact-finding works and so useful for ready and quick reference. For the rest I use one star for a book useful to the beginner: two stars means a fuller and generally more advanced book, while three stars imply the larger and more serious references. These last are only for advanced reader.

THE GENERAL READER

Bengsten & van Royen	* *Fundamentals of Economic Geography* 1942.
Dudley Stamp, L.	* *Intermediate Commercial Geography* 1927.
Patterson, E. M.	*** *An Introduction to World Economics* 1947.
Zimmerman, E. W.	** *World Resources and Industries* 1933.

CHAPTER I

Cairncross, Alex.	** *Introduction to Economics.*
Hicks J. R.	* *Social Framework.*
Leys, M. D. R.	* *Men, Money and Markets.*
Marshall, A.	** *Economics of Industry.*
Dudley Stamp, L.	* *Intermediate Commercial Geography,* Vol I.

226

Newbigin, M.	* *The Mediterranean Lands.*
Pounds, N. J. G.	** *An Historical and Political Geography of Europe.*
Siegfried, André.	** *The Mediterranean.*

CHAPTER II

Carr-Saunders, A. M. and Caradog Jones, D.	* *Social Structure of England and Wales.*
Hays, S.	** *An Outline of Statistics.*
Holman, L. J.	** *Simplified Statistics.*
Allen, R. G. D.	** *Statistics for Economists.*

CHAPTER III

Carr-Saunders, A. M.	* *Population.*
Carr-Saunders, A. M.	** *World Population.*
Malthus, T. R.	*** *Essay on Population.*
Penrose, E. F.	*** *Population Theories.*
Reddaway, B. F.	* *Economics of a Declining Population.*
National Planning Association Washington.	* *Economic Pattern of World Population.*
Stationery Office (Cmd 7695)	*** *Royal Commission on Population.*

CHAPTER IV

Brenan, Gerald.	*** *The Spanish Labyrinth.*
Daryll, Forde C.	* *Habitat, Economy and Society.*
Driburg, J. H.	* *At Home with the Savage.*
Driburg, J.H .	* *The Savage as he really is.*
Dudley Buxton, L. D.	** *The Peoples of Asia.*
Firth, R.	* *Human Types.*
Haddon, A. C.	*** *Races of Man.*
Huxley and Haddon.	** *We Europeans.*
Hutton, J. H.	*** *Caste in India.*
Lugard, Lord	*** *Dual Mandate.*
Macmillan, W. M.	** *Africa Emergent.*
Marett, R. R.	* *Anthropology.*
O'Malley, L. S. S.	* *Indian Caste Customs.*
Page, J. W.	* *Primitive Races of Today.*
Sumner B. H.	*** *Survey of Russian History.*

CHAPTER V

Astor and Rowntree.	** *British Agriculture* (Penguin)
Cohen, R.	** *Economics of Agriculture.*
Graham, Michael.	* *Soil and Sense.*
Henderson, George.	** *The Farming Ladder,*
King, F. H.	** *Farmers of Forty Centuries.*
Mengies-Kitchin, A. W.	* *Future of British Farming.*
Moore, W. G.	* *The World's Wealth.*
Sykes, Frank.	** *This Farming Business.*
Warriner, D.	** *Economics of Peasant Farming.*
Stationery Office.	*** *Agricultural Development in Middle East.*
Royal Institute. Inter. Affairs.	*** *World Agriculture: An International Survey.*
Alexander and Street.	* *Metals in the Service of Man* (Penguin)
Bain, H. Foster.	** *Ores and Industry in Far East.*
Bain, H. Foster.	** *Ores and Industry in South America.*
Jones, W. R.	* *Minerals in Industry* (Penguin).
Leith, Furness and Lewis	** *World Minerals and World Peace.*
McGraw-Hill Co.	*** *The Mineral Industry.*
Tyler, Paul M.	** *From the Ground Up.*

CHAPTER VI

Allen, G. C.	* *British Industries.*
Anstey, Vera.	** *The Economic Development of India.*
Glover and Cornell.	** *Development of American Industries.*
Guillebaud, C. W.	*** *The Economic Recovery of Germany 1933–38.*
Hubbard, G. E.	** *Eastern Industrialisation.*
Lewis, W. Arthur	* *Monopoly in British Industry* (Fabian 91).
Prest, A. R.	* *War Economics of Primary Producing Countries.*
Robertson, D. H.	* *Control of Industry.*
Robinson, E. A. G.	* *Monopoly.*
Smith, D. H.	** *The Industries of Greater London.*
Stamp and Beaver.	** *The British Isles.*

Stationery Office.   ** *Working Party Reports (Cotton, Wool)*.

Nat. Planning Association
  Washington.   * *Post-War Industrialisation in China.*

CHAPTER VII

Arndt, H. W.   *** *Economic Lessons of the Nineteen-Thirties.*

Abrams, Mark.   ** *Britain and Her Export Trade.*
Fisher, Allan G. B.   *** *International Implications of Full Employment in Great Britain.*

Hodgson, R. A.   ** *Introduction to International Trade and Tariffs.*

Jewkes, John.   * *Ordeal by Planning.*
Laski, H.   ** *Communism.*
Lewis, W. A.   * *Economic Problems of Today.*
Lithenthal, David E.   * *T.V.A.* (Penguin).
Richardson, J. H.   ** *British Economic Foreign Policy.*

CHAPTER VIII

Benedict, Ruth.   ** *The Chrysanthemum and the Sword.*
Darling, M. L.   ** *The Panjab Peasant.*
Dennison, S. R.   *** *The Localisation of Industry.*
Embree, John F.   ** *A Japanese Village.*
Fie and Chang.   ** *Earth Bound China.*
Firth, R.   ** *Malay Fisherman.*
Hunter, Neil.   ** *Peasantry and Crisis in Modern France.*

Jewkes, John.   ** *Cotton Industry (Economic History,* Vol. II: 1930).

Rowe, J. W. F.   * *Markets and Men.*
Stationery Office (Cmd
  6153 of 1940)   *** *Report on Distribution of Industrial Population.*
P.E.P.   *** *Report on Localisation of Industry.*

CHAPTER IX

Bastable, C. F.   * *Commerce of Nations.*
Cairncross, Alex.   ** *Introduction to Economics,*

Cole, G. H. D.   ** *What Everybody wants to know About Money.*

Hodgson, R. A.   ** *Introduction to International Trade.*
Robertson, D. H.   * *Money.*

CHAPTER X.

Acworth, W. M.   * *Elements of Railway Economics.*
de Fellner, F. V.   ** *Communications in the Far East.*
Locklin, D. P.   *** *Economics of Transport.*
Ripley, W. Z.   *** *Railroads.*
Ripley, W. Z.   *** *Railway Problems.*
Sherrington, C. E. R.   ** *Economics of Rail Transport in G.B.*
Walker, G. S.   ** *Road and Rail.*
Wedgewood, Sir Ralph L. *** *International Rail Transport.*
Wood and Stamp.   * *Railways.*
Hardy, A. C.   * *Seaways and Sea Trade.*
Kirkaldy, A. W.   * *British Shipbuilding.*
Mance and Wheeler   ** *International Sea Transport* (Royal Institute of Inter. Affairs).
Sargent, A. J.   ** *Seaways of the Empire.*
Sargent, A. J.   ** *Seaports and Hinterlands.*
Siegfried André.   * *Suez and Panama.*
Thornton, R. H.   * *British Shipping.*
Mance and Wheeler.   ** *International Air Transport.*

CHAPTER XI

Bastable, C. F.   * *Commerce of Nations.*
Hubbard, G. E.   ** *Eastern Industrialisation and effects. upon West* (Royal Inst.. of Inter. Affairs.).
Loveday, A.   ** *Britain and World Trade.*
Wright, Philip G.   *** *Trade and Trade Barriers in the Pacific.*
Stationery Office, 1944.   *** *The U.S. in World Economy.*
L. of N. (42. II. A.3).   *** *Network of Word Trade.*
L. of N. (41. II. A.1).   *** *Europe's Trade.*
U.N.O. (1948. II. C.1).   *** *Economic Report 1945–47.*
L. of N. (45. II. A.10).   *** *Industrialisation and Foreign Trade.*

CHAPTER XII

Abrams, Mark.	** *Britain and Her Export Trade.*
Benham, F.	** *Great Britain under Protection.*
Stationery Office (Cmd. 7324).	* *U.K. Balance of Payments* 1946–47.
,, ,, ,,	** *Abstract of Annual Statistics.*
,, ,, ,,	* *Board of Trade Journal.*

REPORTS, ETC.

Abstract of Annual Statistics for the U.K.

National Farm Survey of England and Wales. S.O. 1946.

Survey of the Economic Situation and Prospects of Europe. (U.N.O. 1948. II. E.1).

The Network of World Trade. (L. of N. 1942. II. A.3).

Europe's Trade. (L. of N. 1941. II. A.1).

Economic Development of Selected Countries. (U.N.O. 1948. II. C.1).

Industrialisation and Foreign Trade. (L. of N. 1945. II. A.10).

Economic Report 1945–47. (U.N.O. 1948. II. C.1.).

Europe's Population in the Inter-War Years. (L. of N. 1946. II. A.8.)

The Future Population of Europe and the Soviet Union. (L. of N. 1944. II. A.2.)

Raw Material Policy and Problems. (L. of N.)

International Yearbook and Agricultural Statistics. (Rome Year-book).

The various geographical Journals.

Pacific Affairs.

Foreign Affairs.

APPENDIX TO CHAPTER XII

DETAILS OF EXPORTS OF IRON AND STEEL, MACHINERY AND VEHICLES.

MACHINERY [1]

Machinery	Value 1949 £ million
Textile machinery	24·6
Electrical machinery	22·2
Machine tools (metal working)	14·9
Prime movers (not electrical)	13·5
Boilers and boiler house plant	11·3
Agricultural machinery	9·0
Cranes and hoists	6·1
Pumps	4·8
Printing, bookbinding, etc.	4·1
Other machinery	70·0
Total machinery	180·5

VEHICLES [1]

Vehicles	Value £ million 1947
Road:—	
Motor cars, new:—	
Up to 8 h.p.	8·3
8 to 12 h.p.	16·9
Over 12 h.p.	10·5
Motor car chassis	2·4
Commercial vehicles	9·2
Chassis for commercial vehicles	13·6
Secondhand motor vehicles	2·9

[1] *B. of Trade Journal*, 21.1.48.

Motor Cycles	4·4
Pedal Cycles	10·0
Motor car tyres	6·2
Aircraft:—	
Aeroplanes, complete	13·8
Engines and other parts for aircraft	11·0
Ships and boats (excluding war vessels)	19·0
Rail:—	
Locomotives and parts	8·5
Wagons and trucks (including parts)	5·1
Wheels, tyres and axles	2·9

IRON AND STEEL[1]

Iron and Steel	Value	Quantity		
		Qarterly Average	Third Quarter 1947	Fourth Quarter 1947
	1947	1938	First half 1947		
	£ million	Thousand tons		
Pig iron and ferro-alloys ..	1·8	25	19	13	3
Other crude iron and steel (ingots, billets, sheet bars, wire rods, etc.)	3·8	9	13	12	11
Total crude iron and steel ..	5·6	34	32	25	14
Bars and rods	4·0	26	39	34	35
Angles, shapes, sections, girders, etc.	2·6	25	34	28	20
Plates and sheets not under ⅛ in. thick	3·2	33	36	33	27
Black plates and sheets	3·5	20	18	24	24
Hoop and strip	1·6	9	10	10	11
Total rolling mill products .	14·9	113	137	129	117
Galvanised sheets	2·1	37	13	22	17
Tinned plates	7·6	82	37	42	42
Pipes, cast	2·4	23	22	26	25
Tubes, wrought	12·0	55	59	65	72
Railway material	4·1	40	42	33	44
Wire and wire manufactures	6·5	21	26	23	21
Bolts and nuts	2·0	4	6	6	7
Anchors and chains........	2·0	3	4	5	4
Hollow-ware	4·5	3	14	19	18
Other goods	20·6	64	68	99	82
Total finished iron and steel goods	63·8	332	291	340	332
Total	84·3	479	460	494	463

[1] B. of Trade Journal, 24.1.48.

Summary[1]
Distribution: Hard and Soft Currency Areas.

Class	Hard Currency Areas	Other Areas	
		Sterling	Non-Sterling
		£ million	
IMPORTS	830·3	569·4	387·8
of which:—			
Food, drink and tobacco ..	418·8	268·0	118·6
Raw materials and articles mainly unmanufactured	216·0	210·1	133·7
Articles wholly or mainly manufactured	190·2	77·4	131·8
UNITED KINGDOM EXPORTS	236·5	571·9	328·7
of which:—			
Food, drink and tobacco ..	13·5	32·7	18·5
Raw materials and articles mainly unmanufactured	14·7	4·8	14·7
Articles wholly or mainly manufactured			
Metal goods	103·5	271·1	175·5
Textiles	54·5	128·7	41·6
Other manufactures ...	45·3	115·5	63·2
RE-EXPORTS	18·2	8·2	32·8

[1] B. of Trade Journal, 21.2.48.

INDEX

A

Abstracts & Year Books, 25ff, 46, 82, 89, 94, 108, 131, 145–6, 154, 186, 189, 202, 216
Accuracy, 12
Acworth, W. M., 171
Afghanistan, 20
Africa (Sth.), 5, 60, 61, 91, 94
Age Groups, 41
Air Transport, 182
Agriculture, 72ff, 80, 118, 208
Alexander & Street, 82
Alsberg, C. L., 47
Amazon Basin, 7, 48
Antarctic, 3
Anthropology (ists), 8, 53, 55, 139
Arctic, 3
Area (s), 32
Argentina, 120, 189, 191
Asia, 8, 20, 55, 63, 94, 197
Assam, 51
Australia, 5, 16, 40, 44, 63, 120, 130, 139
Autarky, 106
Automobile (trade), 104

B

Bacon, 121
Balfour (Report), 93
Balkans, 132
Baluchistan, 42
Bank of England, 161
Bantu, 58
Barter, 148
Basch, 165
Belgium & Belgians, 189, 196, 206
Bell, Sir Hugh, 45
Benedict, Ruth, 66
Bengal, 43, 50, 137
Bengsten & Van Royen, 11
Beveridge, Sir W. (Ld.), 123

Bevin (boys), 70
Bible, 194
Bilateral agreements, 165
Bi-metallism, 156
Birth Rate, &c., 38, 50
Black Populations, 61
Bloom, A., 80
Board of Trade, 155
Bombay, 68, 178
Brazil, 106, 183, 197
Bretton Woods, 112
Buddhism (& ists), 56, 118
Bullion, 156
Buonaparte, N., 5
Burma, 51

C

California, 5
Cairncross, A., 10, 152
Calorifics, 23
Canada (& Canadians), 41, 44, 130, 206
Canadian Pacific, 168, 175
Canals, 167, 179–80
Capital (ism), 65, 112, 129
Carr-Saunders, A. M., 160
Cartels, 113
Carter, C. F., 187
Cassel, Prof. G., 163
Caste, 54
Cattle (& Cow), 57
Census (Production), 35
Century, XIXth (see Victorian)
Chemicals, 213
Cheques, 148
China, 11, 20, 43, 50, 79, 84, 90, 94, 136, 158
Churchill, Winston, 161
Clay, Prof., 188, 190
Coal, 23, 50, 82ff, 107, 121, 140, 215
Cohen, Miss R., 80
Colour (clashes), 60–62
Combines & Cartels, 112

236